Introduction

What this book is about

This book looks at the concept of wilderness. Geographers study wilderness regions as part of the overall relationship between people and their environments. In a world where populations continue to increase, and people demand higher standards of living, there is increasing pressure on space. Wilderness areas are those considered to be the relics of once-empty parts of the world, which are increasingly subject to pressures from people and the global economy.

In this book, you will study:

- how Geographers define wilderness areas and why they consider them to be of significance
- why wilderness areas are increasingly perceived to be of outstanding global value for their landscapes and environments
- how recent discoveries and technological developments have highlighted the exceptional commercial importance of wilderness areas and have placed them under threat
- the conflicts between existing populations in such areas and resource developers who may work or live at some distance from the wilderness areas which they would like to exploit.

When you have studied the five chapters in this book, you should be able to answer the following questions:

1 How do wilderness areas pose challenges for and influence human activities?
2 How and why are people a critical component in a wilderness system?
3 How may the relationships between people and wilderness areas be better managed?

How to use this book

The book is divided into five chapters. Each provides a focus upon wilderness areas at a different scale and in different parts of the world; more particularly, each chapter provides a focus upon a different kind of issue. In each chapter, text will enable you to read through from beginning to end. You will need to refer to the Figures as you read. The following additional features are threaded into each chapter in order to help you understand its concepts and its content more easily:

Theory boxes

These help to explain geographical processes which are required to understand the issues in each chapter.

Technique boxes

These help you to be able to present, interpret and analyse data in each chapter. This book focuses especially upon essay techniques.

Activities

These help you to interpret data and text, and work with others in understanding different viewpoints on each issue. Some of these are individual, while others are suggested for groups.

At the end of the book, a Summary will enable you to draw together the concepts and so you can reflect upon and revise your learning.

1 Introducing wilderness regions

Wild thoughts?

Ask a group of people what they associate with the term 'wilderness' and you will probably get several different responses. Some may describe unmanaged areas at the bottom of a garden; others may imagine huge, unproductive stretches of land neglected by human occupants; parents may comment on the state of their teenage sons' or daughters' bedrooms! It is quite likely that some may mention geographical locations – Antarctica, the Sahara Desert, or the Amazon rainforest – with descriptions of wild, hazardous, majestic landscapes untouched by human activity. Each of these responses reflects what lies at the centre of geographical study – that is, the relationship people have with their environment.

In the eighteenth and nineteenth centuries, human exploration of remote areas took place in Africa, Australia, Asia, and North and South America by people from wealthy and powerful European countries. Their views focused on how natural environments could be tamed, and how native populations could be made to adopt the beliefs and lifestyles of those who 'discovered' them. Europeans who colonized Africa often talked of bringing 'civilization' to the 'savages' that they met. In 1776, when Captain James Cook was the first European to arrive in Australia, he described it in Latin as 'Terra Nullis' (literally, 'no-one's land') despite the presence of 50 000 aboriginal people who had lived there for 10 000 years.

A view from the wilderness

In this book you will find that to define the term 'wilderness areas' is far from easy. You will need to think about and discuss various approaches that geographers have taken to identify what and where they are. In reaching your own conclusions on this issue, you will need to take into account the views of the indigenous people who have lived in these so-called 'empty lands' for unrecorded periods. Until recently, such people have been only rarely heard in the debate over the future of the Earth's wilderness regions.

Read Figure 1.1, which tells of the view of Native Americans in the nineteenth century. Many of the 'prairies' to which the Yamparethka Comanche chief refers are difficult lands to inhabit. Like them, many indigenous peoples have survived and in many cases flourished in some of the most extreme climates and inhospitable terrain. Their experience of wilderness differs from the negative view of a 'jungle' (as tropical rainforests are sometimes described) or icy wasteland that is to be feared, tamed and made to service people who live far away with its natural resources. For them, wilderness is home, a place upon which their survival depends, and whose ecosystems must be tended with knowledge and care.

H E I N E M A N N GEOGRAPHY

55J

27

Managing Wilderness Regions

Ian Flintoff • Sally Cohen

Contents

These views are a challenge to many groups who plan to develop such areas. The case studies in this book will often focus on conflicts which result from the widely differing beliefs about the value and nature of wilderness, from nuclear testing in the South Pacific and the development of National Parks in the USA to the global discussions over the future of Antarctica.

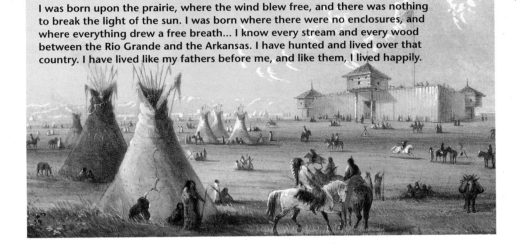

I was born upon the prairie, where the wind blew free, and there was nothing to break the light of the sun. I was born where there were no enclosures, and where everything drew a free breath... I know every stream and every wood between the Rio Grande and the Arkansas. I have hunted and lived over that country. I have lived like my fathers before me, and like them, I lived happily.

◀ **Figure 1.1** A Native American view of wilderness. By Ten Bears, Yamparethka Comanche chief, late nineteenth century.

1 a) As a class, brainstorm the words you associate with wilderness. Try to classify your word lists into categories, e.g. by geographical characteristics.

   b) What images of wilderness areas are brought out in your brainstorm? What are your strongest/most common associations? How do they compare with the image given in Figure 1.1?

   c) How would you define a wilderness area? You may like to compare your initial thoughts with what you have concluded by the end of this book.

2 Refer to atlas pages which show the physical characteristics of the USA, such as relief and climate. What are some of the physical characteristics of the prairies which would make life difficult?

Wilderness regions and conflict

In the twentieth century, concern seems to be much more about the results of 'civilization', with increasing loss of endangered animal and plant species, and damage caused by waste from the processing of natural resources. Consumer-based societies are making such demands on the Earth's natural resources that increasingly remote areas of the globe are being exploited for materials to sustain consumer lifestyles.

Read Figure 1.2, and identify in your atlas where Rockall is located. The 'battle' referred to in the article suggests that people are beginning to place conditions upon future use of the Earth's resources. Figure 1.3 shows a letter from one vigilant organization, Greenpeace, who have been fighting a number of battles to prevent further development of the remote areas of the world. Does the record number of people who join environmental organizations across the world's Economically More Developed Countries (EMDCs) show that the price of economic growth is too much to bear?

▼ **Figure 1.2** From *The Guardian*, 24 July 1997.

The battle of Rockall

Troubled waters in quest for Atlantic oil

As courts hear legal challenge to stop exploration, John Vidal joins squatters on a little bit of empire

From 10 miles away Rockall is nothing but a foamy speck in a million square miles of slate-grey, heaving Atlantic, barely registering on the radar of a gannet.

From two miles, the stump of granite 289 miles [465km] from the Scottish mainland could be a giant barnacled whale, suspended in contorted trajectory. From 50 yards off in an inflatable dinghy bobbing around in a force 6 gale, the perpendicular 80 ft [24m] cliffs are terrifying.

We are seasick after 23 hours sailing due west from the Outer Hebrides, but the landing orders are simple enough. When the rubber dinghy gets under the cliff, we are to wait until the swell is at its highest. The rest is obvious: we must leap on to a narrow pot-holing ladder that hangs down the western cliff.

There have been more landings on the moon than on Britain's most recent addition to empire, and Rockall flirts with anyone who dares to land on it from the sea.

Seventeen oil companies, including BP, Shell and Texaco, were given licences in April to explore the Rockall Trough and the seas west of Shetland for oil and gas deposits. They are already mapping the ocean bottom with seismic ships. If, as expected, their finds are significant and accessible with new drilling technologies, it could extend the global petrol/carbon economy another 30 years.

Ranged against the world's most powerful industry, and harassing its activities by dropping swimmers into the water in front of the survey ships, is Greenpeace. The international environment group argues that to exploit this new oil is economically unnecessary and ecologically dangerous.

Greenpeace seized Rockall on June 10 and renamed it Waveland in protest at industrial development of what industry calls the Atlantic Frontier. In the latest symbolic action, the Queen has been issued honorary nationality of Waveland: her passport is stuffed in a black plastic bin bag behind the brass plaque left by the Royal Marines who in 1955 formally annexed the island for Britain.

Although Rockall and its territorial waters are also claimed by Denmark, Canada, Ireland, Iceland and even the clan Mackay in Scotland, Greenpeace argues that the unexplored north Atlantic should be left to the sea and the birds, a wilderness area of the same significance as Antarctica – which the world's nations have agreed not to prospect or develop for 50 years.

Today, there are few signs of Rockall's previous occupants. Only five people – including now the Guardian – have ever spent a night on the rock.

Oil in the Atlantic

1 Form groups of two or three people. Read Figures 1.2 and 1.3. Try to summarize what the issue is about and why there is conflict.
2 What does this issue suggest about the value that different groups place on wilderness areas?

B.P. WHAT ON EARTH ARE YOU AFRAID OF?

An open letter from Greenpeace following the freezing of our assets by the oil giant.

Greenpeace is an international campaign organisation committed to defence of the environment and the acceleration of human progress. We campaign to persuade governments and industries to adopt cleaner, more efficient solutions that the world and the public urgently wants, focussing on the resolution of global environmental problems.

We believe that our campaign to prevent further development of the Atlantic Frontier oilfields in general, and the Foinaven field in particular, is justified.

None of these oilfields has been subject to proper environmental impact assessment. The potential impact on climate, on birds and on marine life, has not been properly assessed and the UK has only now, nine years late, introduced Draft Regulations to implement the EC Environmental Impact Assessment Directive to the UK Continental Shelf.

Foinaven is a field which has been developed on a "fast track" basis authorised by the Department of Trade and Industry without proper control or assessment.

The state of the North Sea illustrates the fate that awaits the Atlantic Frontier, stretching from west of Shetland to hundreds of miles west of Rockall, if the region is industrialised.

Since August 1996, Greenpeace has urged the UK Government and BP, the main operator of the Foinaven oilfield, to desist from further development. This is not only on grounds of potential direct impacts, for example from drilling muds and discharges, but because it is an expansion of fossil fuel reserves at a time when science shows that the climate cannot sustain the use of reserves that already exist, if the world is to stay within 'ecological limits' of tolerable climate change.

On Monday, Greenpeace wrote to Mr John Browne, Chief Executive Officer of BP, pointing out that according to one of its own studies, if BP were to invest half its 1997 second-quarter profits, or half the monies it says have been invested in Foinaven to date, in a solar factory, then it would produce solar power panels at a cost which would make solar electricity cost-competitive against fossil fuel electricity, overnight.

Greenpeace believes it is wrong and entirely irresponsible for BP to invest in expanding oil reserves when it could be investing in the solution to climate change instead.

Greenpeace notes that John Browne said in a speech on 19 May 1997 that the subject of the 'global environment' was of the 'utmost importance' and that 'there is now an effective consensus among the world's leading scientists and serious and well informed people outside the scientific community that there is a discernible human influence on climate, and a link between the concentration of carbon dioxide and temperature'.

Mr Browne added that: 'The time to consider the policy dimensions of climate change is not when the link between greenhouse gases and climate change is conclusively proven ... but when the possibility cannot be discounted and is taken seriously by the society of which we are part'.

Greenpeace also believes it is wrong and entirely irresponsible for the UK Government to call for tougher controls on fossil fuel emissions at international conventions, while fuelling climate change by a policy of opening up more fossil fuel resources as reserves.

Greenpeace notes that fossil fuel reserves are expanding – for every one barrel of oil used since the 'oil crisis', two have been 'discovered' and added to reserves. Oil use is increasing.

Carbon dioxide levels are increasing. Climate is warming globally at around 0.1–0.2°C per decade. Arctic and Antarctic ice, and mountain glaciers are melting. Diseases are spreading and are forecast to continue to spread, and forests are dying back as a result of the effects of warming. Severe storms and other extreme and life threatening weather events are increasing and forecast to do so by the Intergovernmental Panel of Climate Change. Greenpeace has sent ships to the Antarctic and Arctic to document these events.

At the forthcoming 'Climate Summit' in Japan, Greenpeace will again draw Government's attention to Objective Two of the Convention which calls on Governments to restrict climate change to levels which are not dangerous to natural or human systems and which allow them to 'adapt naturally'.

To meet such limits, it has been calculated that only one quarter of existing fossil fuel reserves may be utilised. To open up new reserves is, in these circumstances, wrong and foolish. The Foinaven field and the other parts of the so-called Atlantic Frontier were conceived prior to the realisation of climate change.

For these reasons, Greenpeace opposes the expansion of fossil fuel reserves by industrialised nations, and seeks instead to persuade governments and oil companies to immediately switch investment to solar power and other renewable energies.

BP is leading the world in the wrong direction by opening up fossil fuels that the climate cannot sustain. Indeed they would rather close down Greenpeace than change direction and invest in solar power.

Greenpeace appeals to the public for its support.

Yours faithfully

C I Rose
Deputy Executive Director
Greenpeace UK

GREENPEACE

▲ **Figure 1.3** Open letter from Greenpeace, 20 August 1997.

The concept of wilderness

Introduction

This chapter will investigate some key questions about wilderness areas:

- What do we mean by 'wilderness areas'? How can they be defined?
- How can geographical research help us to answer these questions? What geographical techniques may be relevant in identifying the location, size and distribution of wilderness areas?
- What are the principal characteristics of such areas? To what extent are such areas outstanding as examples of landscapes or ecosystems?

As you will have realized from Chapter 1, the beliefs that people have about the nature of wilderness are crucial in influencing how they feel such environments should be used. Case studies in this book show that even where people appear to have similar beliefs about the environment, e.g. indigenous peoples and environmentalists, their proposals for the future of wilderness areas can be in conflict.

What do we mean by wilderness areas?

A number of academic experts have tried to define wilderness areas. Many of them now wonder if there are any true wildernesses left on Earth. To identify possible areas, they use criteria such as:

- the lack of human impact on the landscape
- geographical isolation
- inaccessibility by transport systems
- massive size.

Several believe that only Antarctica and some rainforest areas of the world may now qualify. This section will look at Papua New Guinea, Antarctica and the North York Moors in the UK to identify what we mean by 'wilderness'.

In the case of rainforests, traditional views hold that they are 'timeless, immutable (unchanging) ... the crucible of evolution' (Dr Edward Wilson, Harvard University). However, a new generation of academics consider even these areas are as much a result of human activity as of nature. Their research shows that wilderness areas bear long-term evidence of human activity. Michael Williams (Oxford University Professor of Geography) says: 'There is just about no virgin forest ... anywhere in the world. Almost everywhere you go in Latin America, Asia and Africa, you find charcoal buried in the soil; shifting cultivators have always been in the (rain) forests'.

Other researchers have found archaeological evidence that the Amazon rainforest once contained large towns, canals, roads, irrigation and drainage networks. In Cambodia, the famous tourist site of Angkor Wat temple stands close to a former civilization that grew several rice crops a year on what was once thought to be 'virgin' forest.

Papua New Guinea

Figures 2.1 to 2.4 show some information about Papua New Guinea. Figure 2.4 refers to Papua New Guinea as 'perhaps the last true wilderness on earth'. Yet it has 4.25 million people, is farmed and has its own population pressures. Does it qualify as a wilderness?

Melissa Leach (Institute of Development Studies at the University of Sussex) has found that in parts of West Africa, there is often more forest cover than a generation ago, as villagers tend and plant woodland for their own use. She claims that the forest has been used for many generations. On this basis, there may be no such thing as true wilderness, because people have made an impact virtually everywhere. Alternatively, we may need to admit that there are many wilderness areas in the world, and that people are an influential part of any wilderness environment. This may help us in deciding whether or not Papua New Guinea qualifies as 'wilderness'.

▲ **Figure 2.1** Location of Papua New Guinea.

▼ **Figure 2.2** A remote mountain settlement. Steep slopes are cultivated using simple tools to produce 'beds' of sweet potatoes. Population increase and activities such as logging and mining are forcing indigenous communities into more difficult terrain.

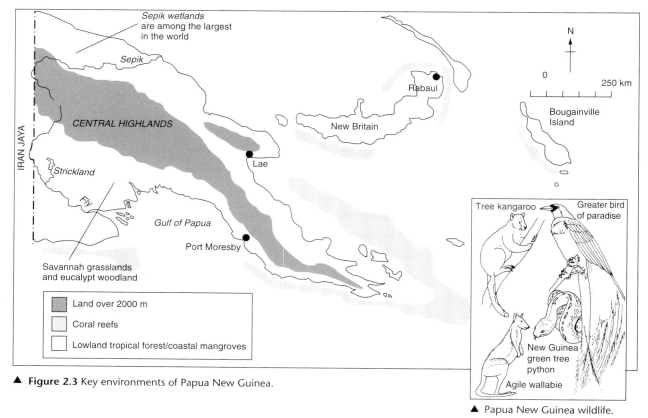

▲ **Figure 2.3** Key environments of Papua New Guinea.

▲ Papua New Guinea wildlife.

▼ **Figure 2.4** From *New Internationalist*, March 1997.

Papua New Guinea is a land of unique natural variety and rich diversity in culture.
Paul Wagner fears both will be lost to the ravages of global competition.

Splendid isolation

The vast, inaccessible land of New Guinea is a magnet for naturalists, linguists and anthropologists, keen for a last glimpse of a passing world. Geographic isolation and a highly diverse landscape have combined to produce incredible biodiversity as well as a rich cultural tapestry.

Geography informs diversity – a fairly obvious statement, but all too often overlooked. 'The Highlands' are a major dividing line in New Guinea, but just part of an astoundingly complex picture. The rugged New Guinean landscape divides the island into hundreds of isolated pockets where flora, fauna and culture evolved together into a unique mosaic.

Sheer inaccessibility has allowed this diversity to survive relatively intact. It is perhaps the last true wilderness on earth, with vast tracts untouched by any technology more powerful than the axe. New Guinean ecosystems are still such a mystery to science that no less than 25

new mammal species have been discovered in the past five years — an extraordinary figure. But modern technology and economic self-interest are pushing into the wilderness faster than we can possibly hope to learn. Whole species and cultures may be wiped out before they are even discovered.

New Guinea's terrain ranges from mountains and volcanoes of intensely folded rock to highly seasonal coastal flood plains reminiscent of monsoonal northern Australia. In between lies the world's most extensive intact tropical rainforest. Offshore there are innumerable islands and reefs, separated from the mainland by deep oceanic trenches.

This allows a huge diversity of plant life. Savannahs of eucalypt and grassland dominate the lowland coast, interspersed with isolated but typically Asian forest patches. The foothills are also forested with Asian-type rainforest, while the upper slopes support a subalpine mix of oaks, conifers and myrtaceaes,

punctuated by herbfields and tree-fern savannahs.

The patchiness of the geology and vegetation has presented an ideal opportunity for species diversity. Two species of echidna, wallabies, tree-kangaroos, possums, cuscus and giant tree rats are among the mammals commonly encountered in the Papuan forest. Dozens of species of small mice, rats, and marsupial insectivores and carnivores scurry underfoot, while overhead glide giant fruit bats, tiny insectivorous bats, and over 700 species of birds, including the famed 'Birds of Paradise'.

Although 85 per cent of New Guineans are agriculturists, hunting has always supplemented the diet and many animals have symbolic uses quite apart from nutritional value. Some species of birds and mammals are known only through specimens provided by native hunters. It is hard to say any individual new Guinean species is 'endangered', simply because the fauna is so poorly understood. But many species are restricted to isolated pockets, making them highly vulnerable to habitat disturbance.

Antarctica

Figures 2.5 to 2.8 show Antarctica, in contrast to Papua New Guinea. Its geographical isolation makes it perhaps the most inaccessible area on Earth – but is it still wilderness? You can consider whether this is the case in the activities on page 12.

▼ **Figure 2.5** Facts and figures about Antarctica (source: *Antarctic Alternatives – Exploring Management Issues,* February 1995).

Physical conditions
The physical conditions of Antarctica result in an environment of extreme cold, high wind and dry atmosphere. Over 98 per cent of the surface is ice-covered and any exposed rock and soil remain below freezing point, except for short periods in the summer. By far the greater part of the continent is a vast cold desert, although microscopic plants and animals can be found in small hollows and crevices in exposed rocks.

Geography
Antarctica is the highest, coldest, windiest and perhaps most beautiful of all the continents, despite its absence of trees and rivers. It is situated around the South Pole, covers an area of approximately 14.25 million square kilometres and is slightly smaller in size than Australia and the United States of America put together. The continent mainly consists of an ice plateau, from 900 to 4300 metres in altitude, and mountains, the highest being Vinson Massif (5,329 metres above sea level).

Katabatic winds
Winds stronger than those experienced in many cyclones, called katabatic winds, are regularly recorded in Antarctica. Antarctica consists of a rock floor on which an icecap has built up. This icecap reaches a height of many kilometres at some places. Katabatic winds occur when gravity causes heavy cold air to pour down the slope of the icecap towards the edge of the continent. Sometimes cyclones form over the sea and when this force is added to the katabatic winds, winds over 120 kilometres per hour may blow for several days.

Population
Antarctica has no indigenous human population. However, every year the countries which operate bases in Antarctica send hundreds of people to conduct research, help run the bases and observe the Antarctic environment.

Long summer days and winter nights
Close to the poles the sun remains above the horizon for half the year and below the horizon for the other half. This means that at some times it is perpetually dark and at other times always light. This phenomenon is due to the fact that the earth rotates around the sun and because the earth tilts on an axis at 23.5° from the vertical. By 21 December the whole area within the Antarctic Circle is exposed to sun for 24 hours a day. By 21 June the whole of Antarctica is in the shadow of the earth and points away from the sun.

Precipitation
Antarctica is the world's driest continent. Precipitation over the whole continent, which occurs mainly as snow, is equal to only 120 millimetres of rainfall each year.

Food chain
The food chain in Antarctica is very finely balanced. If any species is removed from it this will have a great effect on the others. If one species is depleted by humans due to fishing or hunting this could mean that another, or many other species, will die out or not return to Antarctica. Furthermore, if some animals do not return to Antarctica due to a lack of food this will affect other animals.

Salty lakes
Salty lakes occur in the Vestfold Hills. These lakes support only a few specialised organisms. The land on which these lakes are formed was raised from the sea when the continent lost some of its ice at the end of the last ice age, some 18,000 years ago. In the most salty of these, Deep Lake, only two organisms have been found, a bacterium and a green algae.

Fish
Although fish have a difficult time surviving in the cold waters surrounding Antarctica, some have adapted quite well. There are fish which store large amounts of oil between the muscles and under the skin to cope with the cold. Sea water, being salty, remains in liquid form to minus 1.8°C. The body fluids of most fish would freeze at these temperatures. As an adaptation, some fish have an anti-freeze protein in some tissues which prevents them from turning to ice.

Night lights
The Aurora Australis is a phenomenon which is sometimes visible in the sky at night, appearing as beautiful waves of light. It is caused by the sun giving out magnetic particles. This light can consist of many colours such as blue, red and orange. The aurora occurs at the South Pole because this is where the charged particles 'ride in' along the earth's magnetic field. The glow of the aurora is very similar to that of an ordinary fluorescent tube or neon light.

Bases at work
People working in the Antarctic are among the most isolated group of people on the earth. Those remaining throughout winter have no physical contact with the outside world for up to 10 months of the year and must endure long periods of darkness and freezing temperatures.

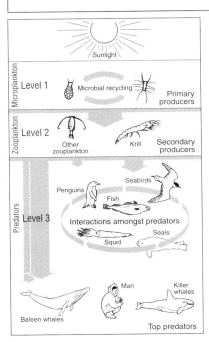

◀ **Figure 2.6** The Antarctic food chain (source: *Antarctic Alternatives – Exploring Management Issues,* February 1995).

▼ **Figure 2.7** The ice-free coastal zone of Antarctica. Only 2 per cent of Antarctica is ice-free and this zone is packed with the continent's wildlife such as penguins and seals in search of breeding grounds and food.

▼ **Figure 2.8** Main physical features of Antarctica.

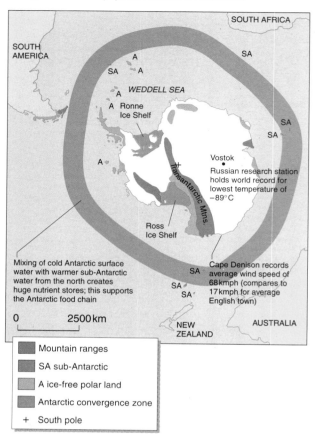

Investigating wilderness in Papua New Guinea and Antarctica

1 Study Figures 2.1 to 2.8 and compile a summary table to illustrate the essential characteristics of these two areas. Use an atlas as an additional reference. Categorize the characteristics of the two areas using the following headings:

- location and degree of isolation from built-up areas
- geographical and population size
- variety and nature of landscapes
- variety and uniqueness of plants and animals (flora and fauna)
- nature of the climate
- density and nature of human settlement/activity.

2 What similarities do you notice in the characteristics you have identified? What differences are there?

3 Which of the two areas qualifies as wilderness in your view? What reasons support your view?

The wilderness continuum

For many geographers, the best definition of wilderness areas is to view them on a continuous scale or 'continuum'. On one end of the scale are those areas where human systems dominate, but which contain small pockets of land with wilderness characteristics. Examples include nature reserves in urban areas. At the other end are large geographical areas which are dominated by natural systems, such as the extensive areas of rainforest left in Amazonia. The continuum illustrates that wilderness quality declines as the economic development process brings roads, telegraph poles, pylons, dams, waste disposal and drainage networks into unsettled areas.

The Australian National Wilderness Inventory maps high quality wilderness areas, using Geographic Information Systems such as satellite imagery. (This process is explained further in the Theory Box on pages 18–19.) It identifies 'pre-European' land cover, so that species of tree or shrub which are non-Australian are used as evidence of early settlement and influence. Further indicators are also used, such as remoteness from permanent human settlement, access routes and the extent to which natural systems dominate (termed 'biophysical naturalness').

This concept of wilderness quality acknowledges that indigenous people, who occupy some 19 per cent of the world's surface, can make a positive contribution to the preservation of high quality wilderness. Aboriginal land uses are studied in Australia in order to learn how to manage wilderness areas which remain. In contrast are the practices of 'European' peoples who have damaged such areas, often beyond repair. Current ideas in conservation use the detailed knowledge of plants and wildlife which have been passed down to generations of indigenous people. Australians now see this as crucial to the success of projects such as setting up or managing National Parks.

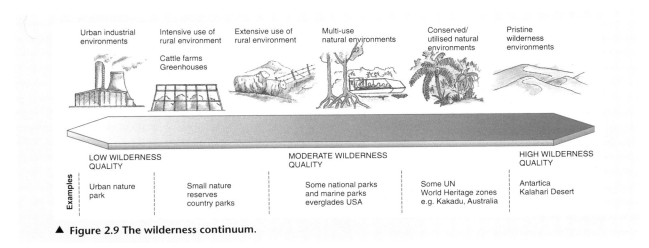

▲ **Figure 2.9 The wilderness continuum.**

A British wilderness? The North York Moors

The North York Moors is one of ten National Parks in England and Wales (Figure 2.12). In general, all the parks exhibit some of the characteristics described within the definition of a National Park as set out by the International Union for the Conservation of Nature and Natural Resources (IUCNNR) (see Chapter 4, page 52). But are the Moors a truly natural area and can they be considered to be 'wilderness'? This section will ask to what extent 'protected' and 'wilderness' areas are the same.

▼ **Figure 2.10** Extract from 1:50 000 Ordnance Survey Landranger sheet 100: Malton, Pickering.

© Crown Copyright

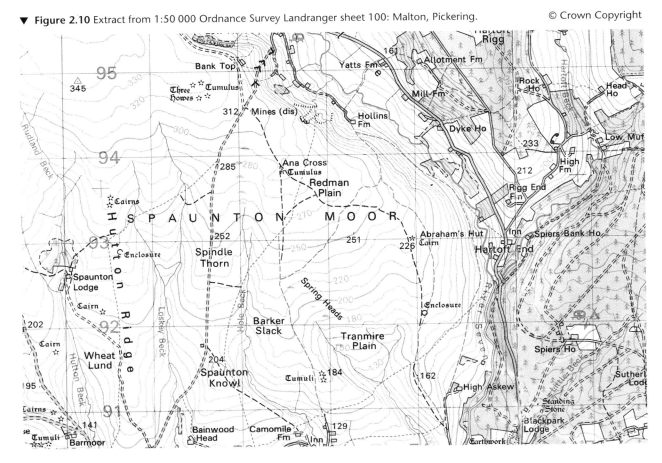

▶ **Figure 2.11** A view over Kildale Moor. The Moors appear to have a remote bleakness which is valued by visitors and residents alike. However, the moorland ecosystem is anything but natural, having been extensively forested from the end of the last ice age through to the Bronze Age. Clearance led to the formation of peat bogs, heather moor and rough grassland.

▼ **Figure 2.12** Visions for the future of the North York Moors. These are quotations from those who live in or near the National Park in answer to the question 'What sort of North York Moors would you like your children or grandchildren to see in 40 years' time?' This was part of an extensive survey undertaken in 1996 by the Park Authority in preparation for its National Park Management Plan.

An unspoilt, sparsely-populated moorland upland which is managed primarily for its special qualities of attractive landscape, quietness and solitude.

Much as it is today – a place to enjoy wide, beautiful landscapes – to walk in peace and solitude yet know that it is a living entity with a working community not just a 'museum piece'. A place where they can see harriers, merlins, grouse, nightjars, badgers and all that has given me so much pleasure. You are doing a wonderful job – keep it up.

This is an area where people live and work and where tradition is strong. I would like my grandchildren to appreciate the beauty, but realise that it must not be exploited simply for leisure and pleasure. I would like to see more trees planted on suitable sites, heather encouraged and bracken dealt with, and plants and animals enjoyed by walkers. I hope that traditions may be allowed to survive.

I have been visiting the NYM for over 30 years and they are still, for me, one of the most beautiful places in the world. I want to keep the sense of space, freedom and peace for my grandchildren. Also the possibility of finding a place where there are few people and a sense of being part of nature rather than part of civilization.

▼ **Figure 2.13** North York Moors: data box. (source: *North York Moors National Park (Student Factfile, Education Centre, The Moors Centre, Danby, N. Yorks, YO21 2NB)*

How the moorland developed

The moorland we see today is a result of thousands of years of human influence in combination with climatic change and the underlying geology.

About 8,000 years ago, the moorland area was covered in natural woodland that had developed after the last ice age ended about 10,000 years ago. The area was first colonised by people about 5,000 to 6,000 years ago. For several thousand years the woodland was burned to bare clearings for hunting and grazing. Trees were unable to recolonise because the grazing animals ate young seedlings and the climate became wetter and cooler, leading to soil changes and the build-up of acidic peats. Heathers and other plants which could survive these conditions became more extensive and as a result the moorland slowly developed.

Now, North York Moors National Park contains several different habitats but the biggest single habitat type is heather moorland. With an area of nearly 500 square kilometres, it is the greatest continuous tract of heather moorland in England and Wales, making it uniquely important for wildlife conservation. Heather moorland is an especially interesting landscape type. It is:

a) the habitat for a range of uncommon moorland plants including dwarf cornel, bog rosemary and wild cranberry.
b) a home for birds that require open conditions, e.g. hen harrier, merlin, short eared owl, golden plover and ring ouzel (the area has been proposed as a Special Protection Area under the EU Birds Directive because of its importance for upland breeding birds).
c) an attraction, especially when the heather is in full bloom and the moorlands are clothed with a carpet of purple.

d) wild and remote, providing a source of rest and enjoyment for many visitors.

Major land use

Landscape type	Square kilometres	%
Moorland	490.62	34.3
Farmland — arable	320.88	22.3
Farmland — grass	289.41	20.1
Woodland — coniferous	213.70	14.8
Woodland — broadleaved and mixed	100.06	7.0
Other	21.54	1.5

Moorland management

Since Victorian times the moorland has been managed by keepers in order to increase the number of territories and breeding successes of red grouse. The heather is burned (or cut) rotationally to provide a patchwork of heather heights. This not only increases the area of heather in relation to other moorland plants, but it ensures a mosaic of older leggier plants for nesting sites and young heather plants with green shoots for food.

Management of the heather by burning or cutting provides a range of heather heights in a 'patchwork' effect and increases the number of territories and breeding success of red grouse. Grouse are shot for sport on some moors if the population is big enough. Sale of grouse shooting rights generates income to offset the costs of moorland management.

Sheep grazing the moorland also generates income. Nearly half of the area is subject to common grazing rights for local farmers. These common rights date from medieval times. Moorland is also important for recreation, it is a valued and beautiful landscape, and contains many significant archaeological features.

1 Study Figures 2.10 and 2.13. Construct a table to summarize map and text evidence which shows how far the landscape of the North York Moors has resulted from a) mainly or wholly natural systems, b) mainly or wholly human systems.

2 Which type of system seems to be more dominant – human or physical? Suggest reasons.

3 Study Figure 2.12. What do people who live in the National Park value? To what extent are they describing 'wilderness qualities'?

4 How far do you agree that the North York Moors are a good example of a National Park as defined by the IUCNNR?

5 Where do the North York Moors fit on the wilderness continuum? Justify your answer.

6 Form groups of two or three.
   a) Investigate another British National Park to find out if your answer to question 5 applies generally to them.
   b) Investigate a local nature area or reserve to assess the degree of wilderness quality represented there. Present your results to the class.

How do wilderness regions change over time? A study of Nunavut in the Canadian Arctic

On 1 April 1999, Canada will turn over 200 000 square kilometres of its Northwest Territories into a self-governing democratic territory called Nunavut (Figure 2.14). This term means 'our land' in the language of its indigenous people, the Inuit. The region itself is characterized by an extreme climate, with mean winter temperatures of –31°C and total daily darkness; it can be said to be an Arctic 'desert' since annual rainfall is between 100 and 200 millimetres, the lowest in Canada. Its population is just 22 000 out of a total Canadian population (1991) of 27 296 860. Its population density is 0.01 per square kilometre, compared with 2.9 for Canada as a whole (a low figure for an EMDC) and 220 for Germany.

Nunavut's three regions contain 28 small communities, mainly Inuit, who have lived traditionally by maintaining a subsistence economy based on hunting, trapping and fishing. However, this region is far from the stereotype image of a barren, frigid and remote land inhabited by 'Eskimos' (a term of derision used by early explorers meaning 'eaters of raw meat').

◀ **Figure 2.14** Land cover in Nunavut.

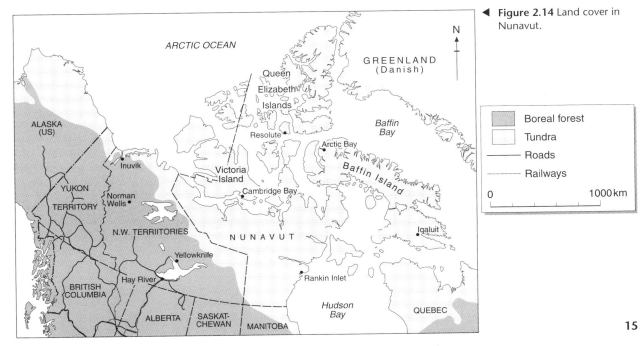

▶ **Figure 2.15** The capital of Nunavut, Iqaluit. Homes may look basic but the growing future capital of 4400 people contains 2500 vehicles on a bare 24 kilometres of road. It is the site of the region's major airfield and a 34-bed hospital and has a very high percentage of internet users.

The historical development of Nunavut

Up to 1576

Nunavut's earliest settlers came from Asia across a land bridge to Alaska towards the end of the last ice age, some 12 000 years ago. Sea levels were 90 metres lower than now. Archaeological evidence suggests a rich variety of food sources for these hunter-gatherers, including woolly mammoth, giant bison, caribou, and seas teeming with seal, walrus, whale and fish. As the climate warmed, vegetation cover evolved to consist mainly of tundra in the coldest areas (inhabited by Inuit tribes) and boreal forest in more southerly areas (inhabited by the Cree tribes).

1576 to 1870

British explorers sought a route across the northern end of North America to reach Asia, and in doing so made contact with the Inuit. The European trade in fur and whales caused damage to the traditional way of life of the Inuit, which was based on a respect for the wildlife and land on which they depended. Many indigenous people lost their lives because of new infections, such as influenza, brought by settlers and traders. Permanent settlements were founded around Hudson Bay by the Hudson Bay Company, and the fur trade drew in many new settlers who made trade agreements with the Inuit.

1870 to 1939

The state of Canada grew rapidly to the north through the purchase of lands owned by the British Government. The Northwest Territories were seen as a vast empty land despite the Inuits' unwritten maps, place names and established hunting territories. Scheduled air services were started, and the Royal Canadian Mounted Police set up posts even in the more remote areas so as to establish control over indigenous peoples.

1939 to the present

Huge changes took place with the outbreak of World War II which were to end the isolation of the north and the nomadic way of life of the Inuit.

- The US military built strategic routes and oil pipelines to link the USA to Alaska, and an air-base was built at Frobisher Bay (now the Nunavut capital, Iqaluit, shown in Figure 2.15) to offer a key air route to Europe.

- Detailed aeronautical maps were made of the Arctic and in the 1950s the Cold War between the USA and the Soviet Union saw the construction of a chain of 5000 early warning radar stations to detect Russian bombers and nuclear missiles.

- The Inuit were made to live in permanent settlements in wooden houses built by the Canadian Government. They were issued with identity numbers on discs because administrators did not understand the Inuit system of names, and schools, shops and health clinics were run by outsiders. Native language speaking was discouraged and in some schools it was forbidden. Hunting activities were strictly controlled.

- An air service into every community has reduced the remoteness; helicopters and aircraft equipped with skis or large under-inflated tyres can land on almost any stretch of land.
- Drilling rigs have been set up in the northerly parts of Nunavut in the Sverdrup Islands to prospect for oil and gas.
- Telephones operate in every community through the use of orbiting satellites, and consumer products available in southern urban Canada can be bought everywhere at a price – a large television that costs Canadian $440 in Ottawa will cost $1000 in Pond Inlet on the north tip of Baffin Island. In the community of Rankin Inlet (population 2100) one in five residents now have an e-mail address.

However, the leaders of the Inuit communities are concerned about the changes to their traditional way of life. They are worried about the impact of money on a people who have always supported themselves. The concept of unemployment benefit (which the Inuit call 'waiting') for the poorest citizens is baffling for many, who fail to understand how people can be given money without some kind of physical effort. Commercial fur trapping and whaling based upon high volumes contrast with the Inuit custom of killing only sufficient animals for their needs. The Inuit hold wildlife in high regard, for they believe that their survival is bound up with the land. Some 40–70 per cent of their diet comes from sources such as seal, caribou and polar bear, and every piece of the animal is used. The Inuit believe that by taking over the government of the new territory of Nunavut in 1999, they will be able to preserve their ancient way of life, and control attempts to exploit the resources of this Arctic desert.

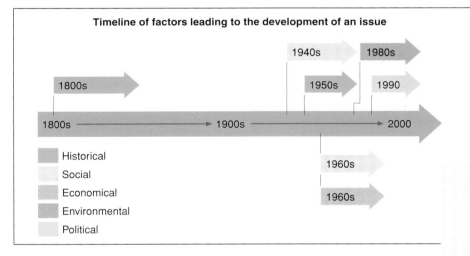

◄ **Figure 2.16** A 'compound' timeline.

1 Research the characteristics of tundra and boreal forest. To what extent are these 'biomes' vulnerable to the impact of human activity?

2 What does the study of Nunavut show about how time can alter our definition of 'wilderness'?

3 Why are people in regions such as Nunavut important in preserving wilderness quality?

4 **a)** Using the information on pages 16–17 and the example of a timeline shown in Figure 2.16, construct a timeline for the development of Nunavut.

b) To what extent does your timeline show increasing pressure on Nunavut? Are the greatest pressures social, economic or environmental?

5 The people of Nunavut have their own website on the internet. Design a 'home' page for the site which describes the qualities of this wilderness region. Suggest information categories to help users learn more about it.

Using Geographical Information Systems to map wilderness regions

A Geographical Information System (or GIS) is the high-tech equivalent of a map. Information which has been collected from different sources about an area can be stored and displayed on a computer. Much information is gathered by aircraft and Earth-orbiting satellites by a technique called 'remote sensing'. Remote sensing means information is gathered about the Earth's surface, using sensors on satellites which measure the amount of solar radiation (electromagnetic energy) reflected back from land cover. Forest will show differently from grassland, water from desert.

As the satellite moves over the Earth's surface, photographic images are compiled. These are updated regularly as the satellite returns to the same area at precise intervals. This gives GIS two main advantages over traditional paper maps:

1 The Earth surface information is updated often several times in a year. Long-term studies of human impact on the natural landscape can be monitored. This contrasts with the difficult and expensive job of updating maps, which is carried out only annually in the case of road maps, or less frequently still in the case of Ordnance Survey maps.

2 Paper maps are static – or like snapshots in time – and lose flexibility. Because they exist as separate sheets, they may be inconvenient if the area of interest lies at the corner of two or four adjacent sheets. GIS therefore enables users to:

- view continuous areas
- isolate or bring together different sets of information as required
- analyze relationships between data.

For wilderness areas, their sheer inaccessibility is overcome by GIS, which may be the only way to find out vital information such as the extent of wilderness over continents, the likely threat posed by human activity, and whether these are changing. Two major national GIS wilderness projects are summarized below in Figures 2.17, 2.18 and 2.19.

▼ **Figure 2.17** National and global mapping of wilderness areas.

World Wilderness Areas Data Set	National Wilderness Inventory of Australia
Sponsored by: United Nations Environment Programme (UNEP), World Bank and Sierra Club (1989)	Sponsored by: Australian Heritage Commission (1994)
Definition: 'Undeveloped land still primarily shaped by the forces of nature'; in searching for 'empty quarters', all areas showing roads, settlement, airports and farming/logging areas were left out	Definition: maps 'natural areas' (an area of land or water which essentially retains its pre-European cover)
Based on: Jet Navigation Charts at 1:2 000 000 scale; wilderness areas which were less than 400 000 hectares in size were not included	Based on: satellite imaging of information based on remoteness from settlement, remoteness from access routes, absence of structures observed in modern society (e.g. pylons, telegraph poles) and lack of disturbance to natural areas
Found: One-third of total land surface is still 'wilderness', continents with most wilderness: Antarctica, Eurasia, Africa, North America	Result: A full set of maps of Australia based on wilderness quality to help policy-makers and environmental managers

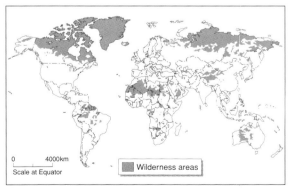

▲ **Figure 2.18** Global map of wilderness areas based on World Wilderness Areas data set (source: Sierra Club, World Bank and UNEP/GRID).

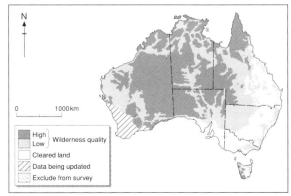

▲ **Figure 2.19** Wilderness quality in Australia (based on National Wilderness Inventory).

Using GIS maps

1 Work with a partner. Study Figure 2.18 and an atlas map of biomes (vegetation regions). What do you notice about any relationship between the distribution of wilderness areas and particular biomes? What conclusions do you reach?

2 What advantages and disadvantages are there in using a large-scale GIS project like the World Wilderness Areas data set to identify the extent of wilderness across the world? What changes would you make to the criteria that the authors used to identify wilderness areas?

3 How useful do you find the National Wilderness Inventory map (Figure 2.19)? Which groups would make most use of such information and why?

Reaching a definition of wilderness

1 a) Form a group of two or three people. Read the definitions in Figure 2.20. Draw a table with three headings:

Summary of the definition	Strengths of the definition	Weaknesses of the definition

b) Summarize each definition in the left-hand column, and then what you consider to be the strengths and weaknesses of each definition in the other columns. In completing these columns, consider the case studies in this chapter, and how complete each definition is.

2 As a group, identify which you consider to be the strongest definition. Consider its weaknesses, and write your own definition of a wilderness area. Present your definition to the class and explain why you consider it to be better than any in Figure 2.20.

▼ **Figure 2.20** A selection of definitions of wilderness areas.

A wilderness area is a large tract of land remote at its core from access and settlement and substantially unmodified by modern technological society or capable of being restored to that state and of sufficient size to make practicable the long-term protection of its natural system. The Society's definition has also been adopted by the Conservation Council of Western Australia (1990).
The Wilderness Society (1990)

A large area with land forms and native plant and animal communities relatively unaltered or affected by the influence of the European settlement of Australia and of sufficient size and shape and location with respect to adjacent land uses to make practicable the long-term protection of its natural systems and primitive condition; which is managed to maintain and enhance wilderness quality values.
The Land Conservation Council (Victoria) (1991)

An area of land substantially unmodified by balanda (non-Aboriginal people), capable of restoration to such a state, where perceptions of solitude, space and wilderness are readily achieved and sustained.
Kakadu Board of Management (ANPWS) (1991)

Wilderness consists of extensive natural areas that are essentially unaltered by people and in which permanent structures or works are absent.
Victorian National Parks Association

Wilderness areas are wild lands designated for their protection and managed to perpetuate their condition and which appear to have been affected only by the forces of nature, with any imprint of human interference substantially unnoticeable.
The New Zealand Wilderness Advisory Group (1985)

... an enduring natural area protected by legislation and of sufficient size to protect the pristine natural environment which serves physical and spiritual well-being. Wilderness is an area where little or no persistent evidence of human intrusion is permitted, so that natural processes will take place largely unaffected by human intervention.
The IUCN Commission on National Parks and Protected Areas (1990)

How to write an introduction to an essay

An introduction is designed to ease the reader into a subject. Most essay titles are written around a problem or issue, to which there may be several answers or solutions. In an essay of this length (you will have 45 minutes to write the essay in the exam), you cannot draw on any more than two or three case studies in detail, so you need to justify those you are using, and say how they will help you answer the question.

The guidance below will help you to learn to plan an introduction. In the section which follows, you will be able to look at the work of one A level student in order to evaluate it, and to judge for yourself what a good introduction might be like.

Planning an introduction

'With reference to a range of examples and scales, explain why the concept of wilderness is a relative one.'

Three things are required:

1 a definition of the meaning of key terms in the title – i.e. 'wilderness'. This makes it clear to the examiner that you know what you are talking about!
2 an outline of the main issue in the title, i.e. that perhaps there are problems in defining wilderness regions, and that we need to take several factors into account, including human activity
3 an introduction to the case studies you will refer to, in order to demonstrate the basis of your answer.

Therefore, in your introduction you should:

1 Define 'wilderness' and the concept of wilderness quality.

2 Explain some of the issues in providing a definition which is based on these associations, i.e. how landscapes we see today may be the result of past human activity, how even areas which may not be remote may possess wilderness qualities, and that definitions change over time and as new technology is introduced, such as GIS. Some

definitions may be linked to geographical factors (e.g. physical – landforms, climate, ecosystems) but many will take the degree of human influence into account.

3 Show that you understand how to use different case studies to support your answer, e.g. Papua New Guinea (and its physical and human environment), Antarctica (and its harsh physical conditions) and Nunavut (to show how time may alter definitions). However, avoid the pitfall of stating any overall answer to the title in the introduction before presenting your evidence. This is what your conclusion section is for!

As a guide, ten to fifteen lines will be sufficient for an introduction.

Evaluating one student's work

The introduction below has been written by a student on the following title:

'With reference to a range of examples and scales, explain why the concept of wilderness is a relative one.'

Many people like to think there are many areas of the world which are still unexplored and untouched by human beings and where ecosystems are still the same as when they were created. Such examples could be Antarctica and parts of the remote Amazon rainforest. These are true wilderness areas and there is no human impact. However, geographers have found that such ideas are false and that the idea of wilderness is relative. In this essay I will use a variety of case studies at all scales to show that this is true.

Form groups of two or three people. Read the introduction above.

1 Decide what the strengths of the introduction are.

2 What could be done to improve it?

3 Write out a better introduction.

Ideas for further study

1 Identify a wilderness environment which you have not studied before and find out what makes it 'outstanding' in terms of landscape or its ecosystem. Create a wall display of your research.

2 Construct a diagram of the food web of your chosen wilderness environment. What makes it especially vulnerable to human impact?

Summary

- Wilderness areas exhibit many different types of landscape, ecosystem and human activity. They can be found at a variety of scales but can be seen to have some common characteristics such as remoteness, very low population density and incredible biodiversity.
- Current geographical thinking supports the concept of 'wilderness' as a relative one, and the idea
  that a continuum from areas dominated by human systems to those dominated by physical systems
  is helpful.
- Areas which appear to possess high wilderness quality, lack of human impact and protection under
  the law, such as the English National Parks, may actually have been changed extensively by human activity.
- Wilderness areas can change dramatically, as new technology allows development of the remotest and most inhospitable of terrains.
- New mapping techniques using GIS (Geographic Information Systems) are enabling geographers and others to study the extent of wilderness areas on global, national and regional scales. Some problems emerge from the nature of the definition of wilderness used in such mapping exercises.

References and further reading

If you are using the internet the following websites are useful:

For Papua New Guinea try the PNG information site on:
HYPERLINK http://lucy.ukc.ac.uk/lien/PNG/pngbcs.html

For Antarctica try Greenpeace on:
HYPERLINK http://www.greenpeace.org.uk

For a journal profiling wilderness areas and current research try *The International Journal of Wilderness* on:
HYPERLINK http://www.wilderness.net/ijw/

Try the Nunavut website on: http://www.arctic-travel.com/

Useful books include:

J. Chaffey, *Managing Wilderness Regions,* Hodder & Stoughton, 1996 (especially Chapter 1).

E. Kempf (ed.), *Indigenous Peoples and Protected Areas,* Earthscan, 1994 (this is full of short case studies of wilderness peoples, land use conflicts and solutions).

The *National Geographic* magazine remains an excellent source of examples of wilderness areas and indigenous peoples.

3 Wilderness under threat: the South Pacific region

Introduction

As you study wilderness areas, you will realize that few are unaffected by some form of human activity or the threat of a proposed economic development, with sometimes bitter land-use conflict. In this chapter the South Pacific region is used to explore some key questions about the threats posed to wilderness areas such as:

- What sorts of human occupancy are typical of such areas?
- Why are wilderness areas under threat? What is the nature of such threats?
- Why are these threats increasing?

Investigating the threats to wilderness in the South Pacific may also help you to consider to what extent similar patterns of conflict are found elsewhere. In Chapter 4, you will be able to analyze ways in which threats are managed in different countries.

The South Pacific environment

Figure 3.1 shows the region known as the 'South Pacific'. This name is given to the region of the Pacific which extends from Australasia across the Pacific to the shores of South America. The region is huge; it takes six hours to fly from the east coast of Australia to Fiji – about the same as it takes to fly from New York to London. Look at its extent, and compare Figure 3.1 with an atlas map of the same area.

The South Pacific was the last habitable region on Earth to be settled by human beings, shortly after the last ice age. Migrant peoples arrived in substantial numbers from Australia and Papua New Guinea in several of the island chains of Melanesia between 1200 and 650 BC, when temperatures were much higher, storms were few and skies were clear. These oceanic migrations continued until settlers reached Polynesian islands such as Hawaii in AD 750. The island ecosystems were characterized by fringing coral reefs, coastal woodlands and grassland and, in some cases, mountainous interiors covered with tropical rainforest.

Small populations traditionally kept subsistence farms with coconut and fruit plantations, supplementing their diet with fish. As populations grew, some deforestation took place. But the impact was small compared to the environmental changes brought about by the European colonizers who arrived in the islands in the seventeenth and eighteenth centuries. In highland areas, the practice of shifting cultivation was widespread but mainly in areas of secondary forest. Primary forest was preserved as 'sacred gardens' for the community, partly out of fear and respect for the spiritual power of the natural

▼ **Figure 3.1** Threats to wilderness environments in the South Pacific.

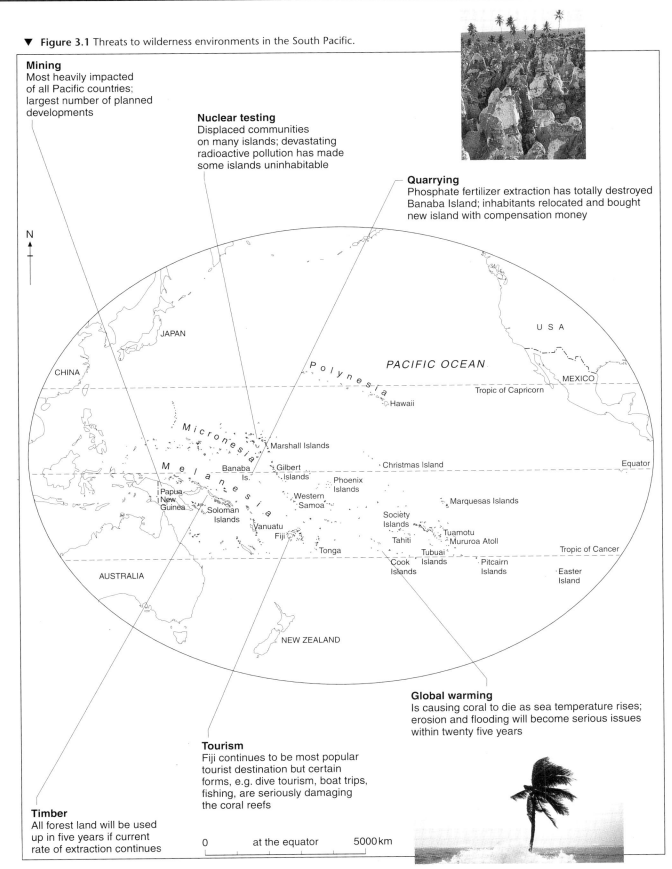

Mining
Most heavily impacted
of all Pacific countries;
largest number of planned
developments

Nuclear testing
Displaced communities
on many islands; devastating
radioactive pollution has made
some islands uninhabitable

Quarrying
Phosphate fertilizer extraction has totally destroyed
Banaba Island; inhabitants relocated and bought
new island with compensation money

Global warming
Is causing coral to die as sea temperature rises;
erosion and flooding will become serious issues
within twenty five years

Tourism
Fiji continues to be most popular
tourist destination but certain
forms, e.g. dive tourism, boat trips,
fishing, are seriously damaging
the coral reefs

Timber
All forest land will be used
up in five years if current
rate of extraction continues

0   at the equator   5000 km

world but also as a buffer against neighbouring tribes. Wealth was based on the ownership of land held in common for the whole community and the trading of shells, feathers from tropical birds and, most importantly, pigs!

Massive change began with the colonization of the islands of the Pacific, especially by Britain and France. British and French traders introduced commercial plantation agriculture, mined valuable minerals of even the most remote islands and displaced thousands of indigenous people from their land. Environmental damage was made more severe by the occupation of the Allied forces and the Japanese in World War II. Deforestation and damage to marine ecosystems caused by the fierce conflict took several decades to be repaired. In the 1950s several islands were used as sites for atmospheric nuclear tests. These were brought to an end by an international treaty in 1963 after they were shown to be capable of spreading radioactivity world-wide. However, nuclear testing continued underground until the early 1990s. Although this reduced the risk, there was still controversy over the extent to which radioactivity was contained. Extensive public demonstrations took place in Tahiti in the spring of 1995 against renewed French testing at Mururoa Atoll; the outcry spread to New Zealand, Australia and to Europe. The social and environmental impact of such testing on remote island communities is examined on pages 33–6.

Current threats to the South Pacific are both regional and global in nature:

- Transnational mining companies are exploiting minerals in highland areas of many islands. The unique ecology of Papua New Guinea is especially under threat from uncontrolled forest clearance and pollution of previously untouched rivers by toxic metals.
- Large-scale forest clearance for plantations, timber, roads and settlement is devastating primary forest.
- The drought caused by the current (1997–8) El Niño event has led to huge forest fires in Papua New Guinea and drastic food shortages.
- Tourism is seen as a money-spinner by many Pacific islands whose inhabitants experience a very poor standard of living and poor health,

but uncontrolled development is damaging fragile marine environments such as coral reefs.
- Global warming could have a potentially devastating effect on many small, low lying islands as sea levels rise; warmer seas are already destroying coral which protects coastlines from erosion and supports some of the most productive marine ecosystems on Earth.

Summarizing the threats to the South Pacific wilderness

1 Use the information on the threats to the South Pacific to create a timeline of human impact (as shown in Figure 2.16 on page 17). Add to this by researching data on CD-ROM (e.g. New Internationalist 'World Guide', 'Encarta') or on internet sites listed on page 39.

2 a) Form groups of three or four. Identify the threats, and write each one separately on a card.
  b) Divide these into suitable categories. Summarize them in a spider diagram.
  c) As a class, try to rank the threats to the South Pacific in order of severity of impact on the natural environment and indigenous peoples. What criteria did you choose to decide your ranking?

Identifying the threats to the South Pacific wilderness

The rest of this chapter will explore different threats to the wilderness areas of the South Pacific. These include logging and mining, tourism, nuclear testing and global warming.

The impact of logging and mining in Papua New Guinea

In Chapter 2 you were able to gain some understanding of the biodiversity contained within the range of ecosystems found in Papua New Guinea, especially within the central remote highlands. However, the long-term stability of these wilderness areas is threatened by powerful economic forces from different interest groups who wish to exploit the abundance of timber and mineral resources:

- The Papua New Guinea Government is keen to develop the country's economy, but in seeking help from the World Bank it has had to relax environmental laws to allow huge foreign mining companies and logging companies to extract its natural resources.
- The fast growing economies of the Pacific, such as South Korea, Malaysia and Australia, and the economic superpower of Japan are looking to exploit the resources of the South Pacific islands. Costs of extraction in other Asian countries are rising and several Asian forests are 'logged out'.
- Many indigenous peoples are determined to bring about an improvement in their standard of living and see the prospect of renting land to mining companies, for example, as a way to better health, education and material prosperity.

What is biodiversity?

Biodiversity refers to the variety of plants and animals found on Earth and the number of species of each. Some 1.5 million species of plant and animal are known to us but, according to the UN Food and Agriculture Organization (FAO), about 75 per cent of crop plant species have become extinct since 1900 and some 4000 breeds of animal are in danger of becoming extinct early in the next century.

The main threats to biodiversity are as follows:

- Loss of habitats is caused by urbanization, commercial agriculture, expansion of roads and new settlement into previously remote areas because of population pressure, and the introduction of tourism, especially in attractive, unspoilt coastal regions. Large mammals such as tigers and elephants are especially vulnerable since they require extensive undisturbed natural habitats; it is estimated, for example, that a tiger needs 25–250 square kilometres depending on the quality of the terrain and that a total tiger population of less than 500 cannot ensure their survival. The number of remaining wilderness areas on the planet of sufficient size and quality is rapidly decreasing.
- Trade in endangered species is rife in many ELDCs. Buyers in EMDCs pay high prices for exotic birds and monkeys, while some animal products from elephant, rhino and bears are prized by traditional healers in countries such as China.
- Transnational drug companies send scientists to ELDCs to search for new species of plant which can be developed and marketed across the world as treatments which will earn them millions of dollars. In many cases they patent the plant product (a legal document giving a company exclusive rights to its sale) and in doing so prevent indigenous people from gaining any financial benefits from plants they have tended for centuries.
- Commercial agriculture by transnational companies in many wilderness areas is based on monoculture (large-scale growing of one crop), where huge plantations of a single species selected for its high yields or its resistance to disease and pests replaces small subsistence plots of several species. Indigenous people, on the other hand, have learned the advantages of maintaining biodiversity since it secures their survival in the face of losses to pests, disease or extreme weather events. Loss of crop biodiversity could put at risk the world's ability to maintain current levels of food supply; the FAO estimate that a 60 per cent increase in food supply will be needed in the next 25 years, much of this dependent on the wild and cultivated species tended by indigenous peoples across the globe.

The Biodiversity Convention signed at the Earth Summit in 1992 by 156 countries attempted to give some protection to endangered species by requiring governments to establish systems of protected areas for species at risk, and to improve damaged ecosystems. In addition, it stated that plants and animals were the property of the states in which they are found and that resource-rich countries should seek agreements with transnational companies and EMDCs so that profits from sales benefit indigenous peoples. Unfortunately, tropical forests which contain at least 50 per cent of all known plants and animal species were not included in the convention.

Investigating resource extraction in Papua New Guinea

Name of mine	Company/country of origin	Activities and impact
Panguna (Bougainville Island)	RTZ/CRA (UK/Australia)	Copper mine currently shut down by war in Bougainville provoked by the effects of the mine. One billion tonnes of waste in rivers has killed all aquatic life in 480km² of catchment.
O.K. Tedi (Bougainville Island)	BHP (Australia)	Tailings from copper mine have killed all aquatic life within 70km² of the mine. Recent out-of-court settlement forced BHP to pay US $550 million to local people. Company still releases 80 000 tonnes of tailings per day into rivers.
Porgera (Western Highlands)	Placer Pacific (Australia/Canada)	World's largest goldmine outside South Africa. Produces one to two million ounces per year; 40 000 tonnes of waste per day pollute local rivers. Hazardous heavy metals found in 140km of river at up to 3000 times permitted safety levels.
Lihir Island (off New Ireland)	CRA (UK/Australia)	Gold mining released 89 million tonnes of cyanide (in contaminated tailings) and 330 million tonnes waste rock into one of the richest areas of marine diversity on Earth.
Frieda/Nena (Central Highlands)	Highlands Gold (Australia)	Open-cast mine producing 220 000 tonnes of copper and 360 000 ounces of gold per year. Mining started in 1998 in very remote, sparsely populated areas. Tailings could affect Sepik lowlands, the largest unpolluted wetland in the Pacific.
Kutubu (Southern Lowlands)	Chevron (USA)	First oil/gas field. Potentially damaging to lowland forests. Oil piped 176km to Kikori estuary. In 1996 non-essential staff evacuated after threats from landowners unhappy over royalty payments.

▲ **Figure 3.2** Some information on mining activities in Papua New Guinea.

▼ **Figure 3.3** Logging of forests in Papua New Guinea – a summary.

Many forests on the west coast of the USA, in Indonesia, Malaysia and the Philippines are now exhausted. Sarawak (affected by major fires in August/September 1997) and Papua New Guinea have become the substitute source of supply for the veneer and plywood factories of Japan and South Korea.

- Each year 20 000–30 000 hectares of natural forest are cleared totally.
- Commercial logging of 5000–6000 hectares is carried out by the Malaysian timber company, JANT, which holds a clear–fell permit.
- Economic infrastructure development (including mining, roads, rail) accounts for a further 10 000 hectares.

A much larger proportion of forestry is 'selectively' felled for prime timber species. Supervision/controls are poor. It is estimated that 100 000 hectares are cleared each year.

Up to 200 000 hectares per year are cleared by indigenous peoples. It is not clear how much of this is primary forest.

The drought caused by the El Niño climatic fluctuation led to massive forest fire destruction in 1997.

We have no water to wash in, and hardly any water to drink that is not polluted. We have no good ground on which to grow food, we have no mushroom ground, no good trees for fruit, no clay pot ground. Our secret places and wild animals are gone, and all our ancient trees are being destroyed.

Quotation from Yalaum Mosel, Bemal village, near to the site of the JANT clearcut.

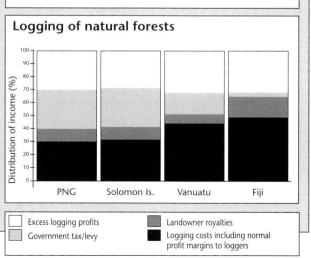

26

Social organization in Papua New Guinea: customary land ownership and 'cargo cults'

Land ownership in Papua New Guinea, like other parts of Melanesia, is based on common ownership or 'Kastom'. This means that it cannot be sold, though it can be leased for 75 years (the productive life of a coconut palm). As a result, poverty caused by landlessness, common in many ELDCs, is rare, since every relative of a land owning family has a right to benefit from its lease, or resources extracted from it.

However, this system has had some consequences which have damaged many communities of mountain dwellers. In several areas, wealthier, educated urban relatives of villagers have leased land to mining or logging companies without proper consultation, in the hope of making a quick profit. One of the results of such actions is to increase tension between neighbouring tribes, partly because of the prosperity of one tribe compared to another, but also because of water pollution caused by mining which finds its way into adjacent tribal areas.

At the gold mine at Porgera, compensation paid to indigenous people by Placer Pacific attracted hundreds of relatives. They demanded their share, despite the fact that some of them had no legal right. Disputes were common, some leading to serious injury or even death. Compensation money is spread thinly and often spent quickly, and there is no land left on which to grow subsistence crops.

However, 'Kastom' can be beneficial to tribes in negotiations with mining or logging companies. Since land is not for sale, more organized communities can hold out for a good deal and use income gained to set up their own businesses and community facilities, such as schools or a clinic.

In the 1940s, when Australian and European explorers, military and religious missionaries first met remote hill tribes, they often brought gifts and wealth not dreamed of by indigenous people. The promise of the arrival of future wealth (cargoes) brought to villagers by foreigners has developed into religions (cargo cults) and thus it is not surprising that approaches from transnational companies, eager to extract timber or minerals, are a great temptation for poor mountain dwellers who are often envious of their wealthier cousins in cities such as Port Moresby.

▼ **Figure 3.4** 'Making the point' – an illustration used in rural education in Papua New Guinea.

▲ **Figure 3.5** The annual meeting of highland tribes at Goroka. This traditional gathering of indigenous people, where participants try to outdance, outsing and generally outdo one another, is now sponsored by Benson and Hedges and Pepsi! Money is provided to stage the show and to ensure there is plenty of free refreshment and cigarettes.

1 a) In pairs, study Figures 3.2 to 3.5. Identify and write down each of the main impacts of mining and forestry in Papua New Guinea.

 b) Use the Venn diagram below to classify these impacts according to whether they are social, economic or environmental, or a combination of all three.

 c) Using highlighters, mark in one colour those impacts which you consider to be positive, and in another those which are negative.

 d) Have the impacts been predominantly social, economic or environmental, negative or positive?

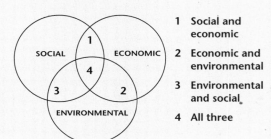

1 Social and economic

2 Economic and environmental

3 Environmental and social

4 All three

2 Imagine you are a wealthy, educated Papua New Guinean living in Rabaul and working for the Government Department of Environment and Conservation. Your relatives in the central highlands have been approached by a mining company to extract gold and copper from your land. When you make a visit to your home village, a fierce argument is taking place between those who wish to conserve traditional ways of life and those who believe that such development is long overdue. What advice and information could you offer? Role-play such a discussion as a class.

3 To what extent do you think that the social organization of Papua New Guinea helps or hinders the protection of biodiversity in the country?

Tourism in the South Pacific

Islands of the South Pacific have environments which look like a holiday paradise for many: long, empty, sandy beaches fringed with coconut palms, washed by warm, clear, tropical seas. Figure 3.7 shows a typical example of how southern Pacific island holidays can be presented to be attractive. Many islands have extensive coral reefs, which are among the most productive marine ecosystems on Earth. These make for excellent scuba-diving, as shown in Figure 3.6. What has prevented mass tourism taking hold is the great distances that most tourists would have to travel to reach the islands, as well as the lack of a typical infrastructure. Only Nadi airport in Fiji can cope with fully-laden Boeing 747 jets, roads are poorly developed and accommodation is hard to come by. All this is reflected in prices which are well beyond the pocket of all but the wealthiest traveller.

 Given the depressed state of many South Pacific island economies, the lure of tourist revenue is a strong one. The quality of environment is the only

▲ **Figure 3.6** Coral reefs. The Pacific Islands region contains 15 to 20 per cent of the world's remaining healthy coral. Specialist dive holidays are seen as a vital income generator for some of the smaller, remote islands.

resource that many small islands have to sell. Study Figure 3.8. Tourist arrivals increased by 6.8 per cent between 1988 and 1993, less than for the East Asia Pacific region as a whole (8.7 per cent) but with great potential early in the next century as more popular destinations suffer from the overdevelopment world-wide of mass tourist resorts. Figure 3.9 shows how holidays with a 'difference' may attract tourists seeking cultural as well as environmental attractions.

◀ **Figure 3.7** Traditional package holidays on Fiji.

Fiji and the Cook Islands

Fiji offers its visitors more than 300 islands of white sand and volcanic beaches, coral reefs, lush forests, colourful local markets and warm hospitable people.

Travelwise
Always carry plenty of small change for taxis and local markets, where bargaining (in Fiji) is definitely the order of the day. As a mark of respect to the Fijians, who are friendly, hospitable, gentle and kind, scanty clothing should not be worn outside the main hotels.

Shangri-La's Fijian Resort

Recommended for:
Singles • Couples • Families

Average transfer time: Approx 45 mins.

'*A firm favourite with families from New Zealand and Australia – number one choice for a relaxing stayput holiday.*'

Linked by a causeway to the mainland, the Fijian Resort is part of the prestigious Shangri-La Hotel Group – set on its own private island in the south-western part of Viti Levu. With a vast range of amenities this is a completely self-contained holiday resort.

Facilities
Two swimming pools • Children's pool, playground and games room • Seasonal children's activities • Five restaurants •Local 'kiosk' for takeaway snacks • Seven bars including disco • Firewalking displays • Traditional music twice weekly • 9-hole golf course • Five tennis courts with clinics – three floodlit • Gym • Watersports including waterskiing, canoeing, snorkelling, windsurfing, sailing, parasailing and in-pool scuba instruction • Volleyball • Table tennis • Waterpolo.

Accommodation
Standard Rooms (sleeping up to 3) are in the Ocean or Reef Wings with one double bed and divan bed, air-conditioning, shower, fridge, tea and coffee making facilities, safe and balcony with seaview.

Deluxe rooms are as above but are more spacious and are in the Golden Cowrie Wing, with bathtub, separate shower, hairdryer and minibar.

The Regent of Fiji

Recommended for:
Singles • Couples • Families

Average transfer time: approx 15 mins.

'*Fiji's finest hotel – combining warm Fijian hospitality with excellent service.*'

Designed in the style of a Fijian village, the Regent is located on a volcanic sand beach on the west coast of Viti Levu. Guests also have access to the beautiful 25 acre Akuilau Island.

Facilities
Swimming pool with swim-up bar • Children's pool • Seasonal children's activities • Three restaurants • Coffee shop • Theme nights • Barbecues and buffets • Live shows • Four bars • Cruises • Golf at Denaru Course • Jogging track • Lawn bowls • Pitch and putt • Ten tennis courts (free during the day) • Volleyball • Free non-motorised watersports.

Accommodation
Gardenview Rooms (sleeping up to 3) with one queensize or twin beds, air-conditioning, bath or shower, hairdryer, minibar, tea and coffee making facilities and balcony overlooking the gardens.

Beachfront Rooms are as above but have direct access to the beach and have one kingsize or twin beds.

▼ **Figure 3.8** Visitor numbers and economic impact in the South Pacific (source: World Bank, 1993).

Package Deals

1993	Visitors (000)	%GDP	Direct employment
Fiji	287	15.7	13 500
Fed. States Micronesia	26	n.a	n.a.
Kiribati	4	6.9	150
Marshall Islands	7	4.5	350
Solomon Islands	12	3.9	496
Tonga	25	6.3	1624
Vanuatu	44	26.3	1300
Western Samoa	47	22.1	1100

▶ **Figure 3.9** Fiji's Hidden Paradise: a different type of holiday.

Fiji's Hidden Paradise

Barry & Nigel Maloney
email: wilderness@wwwdi.com

- Fiji's Hidden Paradise eco tourism resort is a very unique small resort.
- We offer 2 Bures* and a common dining/meeting building.
- Our maximum number of guests is 10.
- Each Bure has its own private bathroom.
- The resort is a fantastic partnership between 2 Australians and an indigenous Fijian Village.

THE DIFFERENCES BETWEEN OUR ADVENTURE AND OTHER GREAT SITES IS EXCITING

- Visitors experience a culture shock along with an adventure of the heart, mind, emotion and senses.
- Guests inform us the biggest difference between this and other great adventures is the friendly, warm, Fijian people.
- Differences between just being a guest or actually experiencing ... sharing and becoming an intimate part of their everyday life is like a gift to you for your lifetime.
- Differences will be seen, felt and heard, providing our guests with an inner as well as outer journey.
- Learning about cultural, social and religious aspects of their society will occur.
- Many guests advise that they cried as their time came to leave 'Fiji's Hidden Paradise' and that this place is never far from their minds and hearts still today.
- These indigenous people will call the dolphins to come and play or swim with you.
- Snorkelling the unexplored, unpolluted beautiful reefs, walking in the rainforests, learning about Bush medicines and relaxing on the beach seem high on guests' list of activities.
- Massage is a normal part of Fijian life ... but we must not offer money for it as the gift will be lost.

* A Bure is a traditional thatched hut

What sort of tourist future for Fiji?

1 Using Figures 3.6–3.9, assess the value of tourism to the economy of the South Pacific.

2 Compare the two types of holiday on offer on Fiji (Figures 3.7 and 3.9) in terms of their social, economic and environmental impact. Which type of tourism offers a better future for Fijians? Can both exist side by side? Give your reasons.

3 What type of tourist development would you expect to see over the next 20 years in Fiji and other islands? Investigate other areas of tourist development in wilderness environments, such as Florida's Everglades, Australia's Great Barrier Reef or Phuket in Thailand.

Dive tourism in the South Pacific

The dilemma faced by many islands is that they depend for their economic well-being on the use of a beautiful but vulnerable natural environment. Indigenous people value their traditions and the wilderness quality of their islands, but are growing impatient with the lack of basic services such as a clean water supply and electricity. Even the most environmentally aware of tourists usually expect certain comforts (cold beer, showers, fast access to bigger resorts), which are still unusual in more remote locations. The extent to which such needs can be met for growing numbers without causing lasting damage is a matter of debate.

▼ **Figure 3.10** Extracts from Radio Australia about dive tourism in the Pacific.

COURT: This week on 'One World' the focus is on scuba diving tourism and the marine environment. Dive tourists are providing a significant part of the tourism dollar in the Pacific, especially in Fiji, the Solomon Islands and in parts of Micronesia. Palau in particular has become renowned as a world class diving spot and is attracting thousands of people a year. As many listeners will know, coral reefs are already under a lot of pressure. Threats include natural climatic events, damaging fishing practices such as dynamite fishing and cyanide poisoning, coral bleaching, saltation from coastal erosion and anchor damage. It's been estimated that about 70 per cent of the world's coral reefs are degraded or destroyed. So is dive tourism another threat to coral reefs or can the diving industry play a role in protecting these fragile areas?

It's clear that inexperienced divers can do quite a bit of damage to coral reefs. Sometimes divers assume that souveniring bits of coral and shells while they're diving won't affect a reef system. Divers can also knock coral with their hands and flippers when they don't have their buoyancy vests under control. Even experienced divers who are photographers can damage coral in their enthusiasm to get a good shot. Anchors thrown overboard from diving boats can smash coral and even urine from divers can affect corals if people are diving in big enough numbers. This is the bad news about diving and some diving areas have been severely degraded by diving pressure. Diving photo journalist Tim Rock talks about the vulnerability of reefs to outside impact.

ROCK: I'm not real sure exactly how much impact divers have and some of the less travelled areas that you can see the impact, in places like the Virgin Islands National Park, have made snow point trails and people would stop and take a look and that basically wore out the corals. The same thing happened on Florida's coral keys down there. And sometimes when people get on in their part of the world and see how lush and rich it is out here, they think that the reef has like an infinite ability to bounce back. But Guam here has had its sure problems due to over-development and continued use of summer ferries that has allowed algae blooms to take over and basically smother the corals and the reefs that haven't returned in five or six years, so you know the ocean is a lot more fragile than people. Actually it really needs a lot of care.

COURT: Francis Toribiong has been diving for over twenty years and for most of these has been taking divers out to dive Palau's famed coral reefs. He's seen an obvious decrease in the number of fish, especially large fish on the reefs. He says this is not due to dive tourists but he does see a definite need for a strategy to manage dive tourism in Palau.

TORIBIONG: The corals are still there, the divers are not really that measure of problem to the reefs. The problem to the reefs is the storm, the tropical storm that comes through the island and destroys the reef. The sewage outfall from nearby shorelines created another problem. The population of fish have been depleted, I would say about 70 per cent of our fish have been taken away. Not because of our divers – I can talk about something else. Since the Palau economy has grown, a lot of people have access to the ocean, they have their own boat, they've got their own fast boat and the new technical fishing, bottom fishing with fishing lines – we didn't have so much fishing line in the old days. And I've been trying to change the attitude – that you can be a man without even killing a big fish or killing a lot of fish, so the population have gone down quite a bit and the reefs are still beautiful reefs. Of course there's still minor problems through the divers who would hit the corals and knock down the corals.

The divers nowadays are more environmentalist, conservationists because they are talking about conserving the reef.

The formation and ecology of coral reefs

Coral reefs are among the world's oldest (5000–10 000 years) and most productive ecosystems. Often described as the marine equivalent of the tropical rainforest, a single reef may contain 3000 species of coral. Globally, coral reefs support one-third of all marine fish. Their importance to human populations lies not only in their ability to provide rich food sources, but also in their role in protecting coastlines by reducing the power of incoming waves. Recent coral reef destruction in Sri Lanka led to one shoreline being eroded some 300 metres over ten years. When they die, corals form limestone shells. These remove carbon dioxide from the atmosphere and play a vital role in reducing the impact of greenhouse gases which cause global warming.

Corals are tiny sea creatures, or polyps, which are related to sea anemones. They exist in large colonies and depend for their growth on an algae which lives on the surface of the polyp, and creates food for it by photosynthesis. The algae gain a protected habitat, and use some of the polyp's body fluid and mineral waste. The algae give corals their colour and provide food for abundant marine life. Corals only grow in tropical and subtropical seas where specific conditions are met:

- water temperatures of not less than 21°C and not more than 30°C
- shallow seas of a depth not greater than 35 metres to allow photosynthesis
- clear, well oxygenated water with plentiful microscopic plankton on which to feed.

Coral reefs and atolls are thought to have built up very slowly over hundreds of thousands of years, as shown in Figure 3.11. Their origin seems to be related to volcanic activity. Over time, a sinking volcanic cone or rising sea level may create a reef of coral.

Figure 3.12 shows how coral reefs are under threat from a range of human activities in the South Pacific, and from natural pressures such as seasonal flooding and tropical storms. These coat coral in sediment, thereby preventing photosynthesis, and make them liable to damage from natural predators such as the Crown of Thorns jellyfish.

▼ **Figure 3.11** Atoll formation.

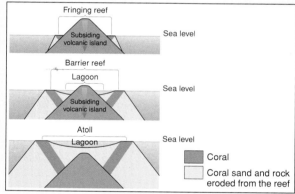

Threat	Example	Threat	Example
Over-collecting		*Coastal development*	
Fish	Futuna Island, France	Causeway construction	Canton Atoll, Kiribati
Giant clams	Kadavu and islands, Fiji	Sand mining	Moorea, French Polynesia
Pearl oysters	Suwarr Atoll, Cook Islands	Roads and housing	Kenting National Park, Taiwan
Coral	Vanuatu	Dredging	Johnston Island, Hawaii, USA
Fishing methods		*Pollution*	
Dynamiting	Belau, USA	Oil spillage	Easter Island, Chile (1983)
Breakage	Vava'u Group, Tonga ('tu'afeo')	Pesticide spillage	Nukunonu Atoll, New Zealand (1969)
Poison	Uvea Island, France	Urban/industrial	Hong Kong
Recreational use		Thermal	Northwestern Guam, USA
Tourism	Heron Island, Great Barrier Reef, Australia	Sewage	Micronesia
Scuba diving	Hong Kong	*Military*	
Anchor damage	Molokini Island, Hawaii, USA	Nuclear testing	Bikini Atoll, Marshall Islands (1946–58)
Siltation following land clearance		Conventional bombing	Kwajalein Atoll, Marshall Islands (1944)
Fuelwood collection	Upolu Island, Western Samoa		
Deforestation	Ishigakishima, Yaeyama-retto, Japan		

◄ **Figure 3.12** Human-induced threats to coral reefs in the Pacific Ocean (after N. Middleton, *The Global Casino*, Edward Arnold, 1995).

1 In what senses may coral reefs be said to be 'fragile'?

2 Identify the key threats to coral reefs identified in Figures 3.10 and 3.12.

3 How may scuba diving damage coral? Figure 3.10 indicates that there is some debate about the actual damage caused by diving compared to other activities. Summarize the key points in the debate with one other person.

4 In groups, decide after discussion whether there are ways in which tourism can be allowed to continue without causing lasting damage to the reefs. Is tourism more acceptable as an economic activity than other examples in this chapter?

5 Use Figure 3.13 to help you construct a conflict matrix on dive tourism in the South Pacific. How serious are the conflicts?

Constructing a conflict or involvement summary matrix

Many issues involving land use conflict include a wide range of groups or individuals whose values are very different. They are therefore likely to propose different futures for the same place. In trying to summarize either the relative involvement of groups or the conflicts between these groups, you can construct a matrix. The completed matrix allows you to see at a glance where key involvements or conflicts lie, and to highlight the strength of the conflict by the simple use of colour, as seen in Figure 3.13. This particular technique is useful for a range of geographical enquiries, but especially in decision-making exercises where there are many sources or many points of view about an issue.

▼ Figure 3.13 A conflict matrix. The individual instances of conflict are shown as crosses and the level of conflict by colour.

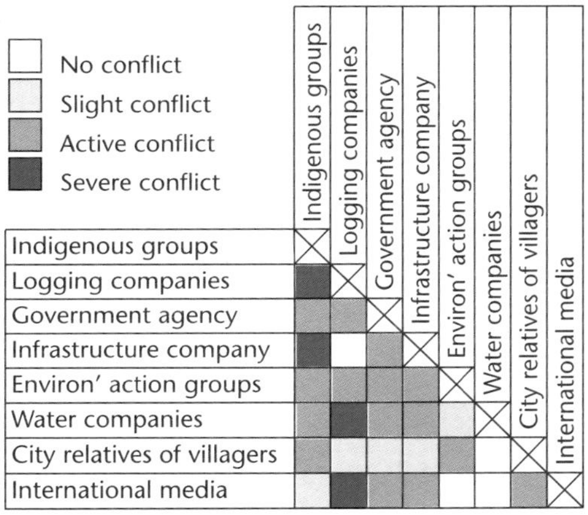

The effects of nuclear testing on wilderness areas in the South Pacific

Land means a great deal to the Marshallese. It means more than just a place where you can plant your food crops and build your houses; or a place where you can bury your dead. It is the very life of the people. Take away their land and their spirits go also.

▲ Figure 3.14 Petition from the leaders of the Marshall Islands to the United Nations, March 1956, requesting an end to US nuclear testing.

The use of remote Pacific atolls by the US and British governments for early atmospheric nuclear testing, and more recently, by the French government for underground nuclear testing remains a source of great sadness and anger for the inhabitants of the islands concerned. The testing in different time periods was concentrated in three areas:

- The earliest atmospheric nuclear testing in the Pacific was by the USA in 1946 in the Marshall Islands. Testing continued until the early 1960s when operations were switched to the Nevada Desert.

- British atmospheric nuclear tests were initially carried out on Christmas Island in the 1950s and then continued in Australia until the early 1960s. Later British underground nuclear tests were conducted for Britain by the USA in Nevada under the terms of a bilateral defence agreement.

- French underground nuclear tests were carried out in the Polynesian Islands, notably Mururoa and Fangataufa Atolls, from 1966. The major nuclear weapon states agreed to stop nuclear testing in the early 1900s but France continued with underground testing until international protest brought them to an end in 1995.

In the period immediately after 1945, the USA continued its development of nuclear weapons. The Soviet Union, fearing the military power of the USA, quickly developed its own nuclear weapons and both countries began an extensive series of nuclear tests. In turn, although with many fewer tests, they were followed by Britain, France, China and India. For the USA, then Britain and later France, the temptation to use remote South Pacific territories as testing sites proved irresistible. The islands were chosen for their remoteness from large centres of population and low population density.

The degree of secrecy imposed by the USA prevented the general public from knowing about the plight of South Pacific islanders involved in atmospheric nuclear testing by the USA until the 1980s and 1990s, when previously confidential US government papers were released. These showed that many islanders were exposed to significantly high levels of radioactive fallout on occasion when the predicted wind directions for high yield tests proved wrong.

The use of wilderness environments and remote communities as sites for nuclear testing and waste dumping, as well as the disposal of toxic wastes, is all too common. The desert state of Kazakhstan in the former Soviet Union is extensively polluted by nuclear testing, and birth defects are common in the remote village populations. In May 1998, India detonated five nuclear devices in the desert of Rajasthan.

The Marshall Islands: long-term effects of nuclear testing

Few people suffered more from nuclear testing than those who lived on the US site of Bikini Atoll. In 1946, all 167 inhabitants were resettled on the nearby island of Rongerik, shown in Figure 3.15. Bikini was selected because it was much higher above sea level than most atolls; it was large and had easy access by ship to its central, protected lagoon.

Early tests were 'atmospheric' (i.e. conducted on land) and many Marshallese were exposed to very high levels of radioactive fallout. In 1954 the 'Bravo' bomb, some 1000 times more powerful than that used over Hiroshima in Japan in 1945, was exploded on Bikini, despite weather reports indicating that winds were blowing towards other inhabited islands. Rongelap residents (Figure 3.15) experienced a covering of gritty white ash as the fallout from the bomb reached the island, and symptoms such as nausea, vomiting, itchy skin, and eye and skin burns were common. It was 48 hours before an evacuation to the US base at Kwajalein was ordered to take place, by which time most residents had ingested dangerous levels of radioactive dust or fish. Altogether 'Bravo' contaminated 18 of the 23 atolls that make up the Marshall Islands.

Meanwhile, the Bikinians had run out of food on Rongerik Atoll. It had a smaller, lower lying land area which was periodically flooded by high tides.

▼ **Figure 3.15** Movements of Marshallese from US nuclear testing.

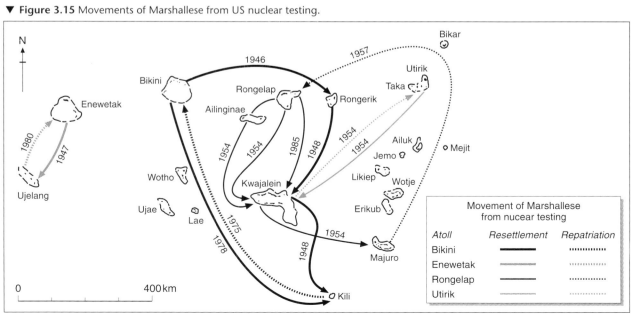

The fish had been contaminated by testing on Bikini. On the verge of starvation, they were rescued by US Navy doctors and moved to Kili Atoll, a single island with no lagoon or protected anchorage. Ships could not deliver food, and fishing could not take place because of the rough surf; the US Navy had to rescue the islanders again by organizing emergency airdrops!

In recent years, life has improved with the construction of a power plant and an airport which allows planes to land each week. However, a self-sufficient way of life has been replaced with total dependence on the USA and a diet of tinned food. The US Government has promised to return the Bikinians to their former home, but a previous attempt in 1978 was abandoned due to high levels of caesium 137 (a radioactive substance) discovered in the first crops to be grown. Lawsuits and lobbying by the Bikinians themselves have forced the US Government to set up a US $110 million trust fund to clean up the islands, but this will not cover all 23 islands. Some islands will never be safe to return to; in 1982, contaminated topsoil from Enewetok was dumped on Runit Atoll and covered with a 115-metre wide concrete dome, but cracks in the container found in the 1990s mean that Runit will remain radioactive for 25 000 years!

Health problems are widespread in the Marshall Islands. A survey of residents in 1976 showed that 69 per cent of Rongelap children who were under ten years of age at the time of the Bravo bomb in 1954 had developed thyroid cancer. In 1997,

thyroid cancers were still over 100 times more common than the world average.

Mururoa: nuclear testing, the economy and the environment

Mururoa seemed an ideal testing site for France to conduct underground nuclear tests in that only 5000 people lived within a 1000–kilometre radius of the site. The nearest inhabited island (Tureia) is 100 kilometres away and Tahiti is 1200 kilometres distant. However, whereas all other underground nuclear tests have been successfully contained in deep shafts or long tunnels in hard rock, Mururoa is built up from coral. Separate shafts had to be drilled for each test and appropriate means developed to seal the shaft immediately after detonation to retain all the radioactive products below ground.

The long-term effects of nuclear testing on the health of Pacific islanders are well documented for the US atolls, but this contrasts with the secrecy which surrounds similar tests in French Polynesia. The French Government has not published any of its research findings, and has only allowed two research teams to study the environmental effects on Mururoa; one led by the French scientist Jacques Cousteau in 1987, and one by Greenpeace in 1994. In both cases the teams were allowed a maximum of five days and could go only to specific locations identified by the French Government. The general findings are shown in Figure 3.16.

▼ **Figure 3.16** The environmental effects of testing on Mururoa Atoll.

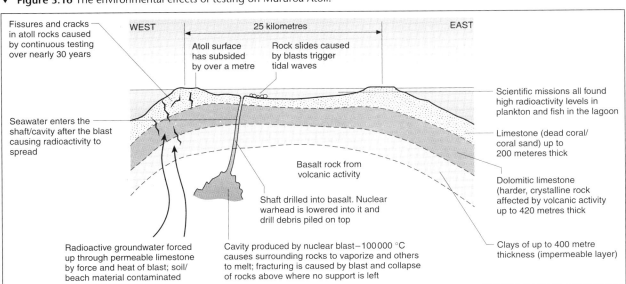

Only one survey of the health effects on Polynesians has been carried out to date by the international relief agency, Médecins Sans Frontières, in 1995. However, there are no major conclusions to the project since much of the relevant information is not available for several key reasons:

- The official register of cancers for French Polynesia only began in May 1985, so no reliable data are available for long-term studies. The Public Health Ministry in Tahiti still estimates that fewer than 60 per cent of cancers are recorded.
- Death certificates only became compulsory in 1981 and cause of death is not always certified by a doctor, especially in remote atolls.
- No statistics exist for birth defects in children, so the study of long-term effects on families affected by nuclear testing is not possible. This is a major problem because often ten to thirty years pass before the worst effects of radioactive poisoning are known.
- The French Government has no plans to study the health of the 13 000 nuclear site workers who were most at risk.

However, many French Polynesians feel that nuclear testing and their French colonial rulers have brought them a standard of living well above that of their Melanesian and Micronesian cousins. Their average income is three times that of Fiji, and in 1995 alone France invested US $1.5 billion in the islands. The French have promised to subsidize the economy until 2006 to compensate for loss of income caused by the end of nuclear testing, since about 50 per cent of the 79 000 jobs are in government-related employment.

Nevertheless, not all Polynesians enjoy the same higher standard of living. Urban centres such as Papeete, the main city on Tahiti, is drawing young migrants from the more remote islands of the Marquesas, where traditional subsistence ways of life are seen as far less attractive. New developments in the production of black pearls from the Marquesas atolls are beginning to stop the flow of migrants, but for many the commercial world has changed their way of life for ever.

Analyzing the effects of nuclear testing in the South Pacific

1 Identify the key costs and benefits of nuclear testing in the South Pacific. Design a conflict matrix (see Figure 3.13) for the main participants in the issue, such as the French and US Governments, islanders' lobby groups, nuclear industry workers, representatives of the fishing and tourist industries, environmental groups such as Greenpeace and others you consider to be involved.

2 Identify how and why the main participants are likely to conflict.

3 Based on the conflict matrix, organize a debate to consider whether:
  a) nuclear testing should continue

  b) the use of wilderness areas such as the South Pacific region should be considered for high-risk testing, such as nuclear weapons.

Take a vote and discuss the results of it as a class.

4 After the debate, summarize the main social, economic and environmental effects of testing presented both by those in favour of and those against testing. Which points influenced your own point of view most?

5 In developing the idea of a 'World Park' for Antarctica to preserve its wilderness quality, Greenpeace wanted to keep it a nuclear-free zone. Would you support such an idea for the South Pacific? What would be the pressures in favour of and against such an idea?

Global warming: the final straw for the South Pacific?

Among the most vocal groups at the world leaders' climate conference at Kyoto in Japan in December 1997 were the representatives of South Pacific nations. The purpose of the conference was to set targets for reductions in carbon dioxide emission, which is the principal cause of global warming. Pacific islands pressed for ambitious targets to be set for the main world polluters, since rises in sea level – projected to be up to a metre over the next century – could cause many islands to be flooded beyond repair. In the event, only a very modest target for emission reduction was agreed and few Pacific nations feel that EMDCs have taken seriously the threats they are facing.

The nature of the threat from rising sea levels is related to several different factors:

- Many island nations such as Kiribati, Marshall Islands, Tokelau and Tuvalu have very small populations and small land areas, but all have land rises of less than 4 metres above mean sea level. The islands are also built mainly from loose coral sand and gravel which is thrown up during large storms onto surrounding reefs.
- Even on higher islands such as Fiji, 90 per cent of the population lives along the coast because of the traditional subsistence fishing–farming way of life. Rising sea levels are already causing extensive erosion of beaches and surrounding reefs. This in turn leads to greater flood risk from both marine and freshwater sources, forced up by the pressure of the rising sea surface.
- Sea water is beginning to penetrate into coastal freshwater aquifers as the water table is forced to rise, and crop yields are showing signs of falling as a result.
- Many coastal tourist resort owners are spending huge amounts of money to maintain beaches which were maintaining themselves only 50 years ago. Proposals for ambitious schemes to develop new resorts on land reclaimed from the sea seem to ignore the threat of rising sea levels.

Many Pacific Governments feel that it is the responsibility of countries such as Japan, the USA and Britain to provide funds for coastal protection, since they are seen to be the greatest polluters. Islanders, on the other hand, will feel the greatest effects of rising sea levels, having had a very small influence on climate change (Figure 3.17). Some projects are underway such as a Japanese-funded sea wall to protect the Tongan capital of Nuku'alofa, but it is unlikely that remote atoll communities will be given the same degree of protection.

Coral reefs are already under threat from a range of human activities, as described earlier on pages 31 and 32. However, ocean temperature rise can cause entire reefs to die. When water surrounding a coral is heated beyond 32°C, it can eject the symbiotic algae which lives within it and gives it the array of colours typical of coral reefs. The coral then becomes 'bleached' and dies, a symptom of global warming already observed in parts of French Polynesia and the Cook Islands. The result is the destruction of reefs, and the loss of a natural protective buffer against huge waves whipped up by tropical storms or by undersea earthquakes.

◀ **Figure 3.17** Daydream Island, Fiji. This idyllic but low-lying island is in danger of being destroyed by rising sea levels within the next 20 years. It is ironic that for many wilderness communities in the Pacific the future of their home, which they have tended carefully over thousands of years, is at risk because of the abuse of the planet by those who live thousands of kilometres away.

Using case studies to develop answers in essays

One of the purposes of an essay is to show your ability to develop an argument, using examples of case studies. It is not just to show how much factual material you have learnt. You need to know your material and to be familiar with case studies. But the main point is for you to understand how case studies can help to establish ideas or arguments. Once you have grasped ideas, you need to show how well you can support them with factual material.

A high proportion of marks in essays are for analysis and evaluation. This means you must analyze material to answer the question, and evaluate the answer you have reached at the end of the essay. To develop your essay, follow these guidelines. The guidance here is about writing an essay on the title:
'Explain how and why many of the world's wilderness regions are increasingly under threat from economic development. You should illustrate your answer with case studies of at least two contrasting areas.'

Planning and writing – using a spider diagram to plan

The key to using case studies effectively in an essay is to be selective with your material by breaking down your answer at the planning stages into several sections – probably the paragraphs you will use – in something like a spider diagram. In an essay, you will be assessed on ideas that you illustrate with case studies, not just on writing factual material. These ideas are your main points. Look at the spider diagram in Figure 3.18. It contains case studies which are used to support the essay – both *how* wilderness regions are under threat, and *why*.

▼ **Figure 3.18** Spider diagram for the essay title – a student's plan for the main body of the essay.

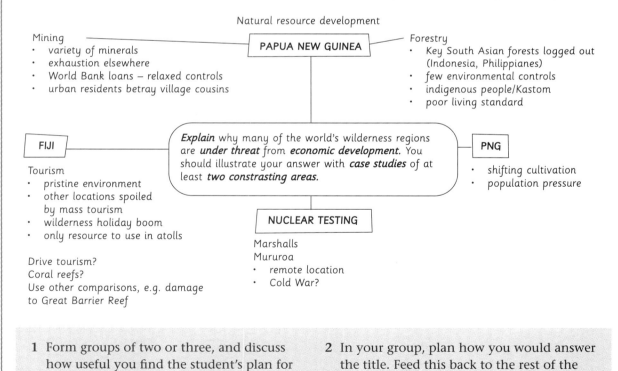

1 Form groups of two or three, and discuss how useful you find the student's plan for the main essay, shown in Figure 3.18. What are the main strengths and weaknesses in its use of case studies?

2 In your group, plan how you would answer the title. Feed this back to the rest of the class. Which case studies have been chosen and why?

Ideas for further study

1 a) Make a collection of articles from newspapers, magazines, CD-ROM or the internet about conflicts in wilderness areas of the world.

  b) Classify the articles according to the nature of the threat and causes shown. What conclusions do you reach? Have you identified any threats which are not discussed in this chapter? What are they?

2 Create a file of relevant case studies of wilderness areas from your studies so far using the classification you have used for question 1 above. Review some past A level essay titles on wilderness areas, and select the most relevant case studies to use.

Summary

- The South Pacific region contains marine and land ecosystems of outstanding quality and variety.
- Threats to the South Pacific wilderness come from many different human activities; those with greatest direct impact include mining, forestry, tourism, nuclear testing and toxic waste dumping. In all cases, the threats come from the availability of an immense variety of natural resources which exist in a form largely unused by its indigenous peoples.
- Biodiversity is under enormous pressure, even in some of the most remote regions such as the mountainous region of central Papua New Guinea; indigenous peoples face great dilemmas about how their land should be used.
- Customary land ownership and traditional attitudes to its use complicate the nature of conflicts over its use.
- Tourism is set to increase dramatically in the region. Pressures on coral reefs which are fundamental to life on the islands are proving serious, and the resource that tourists most value, the beaches and reefs, are at risk.

- Nuclear testing in remote island communities has had devastating long-term social, economic and environmental consequences. Much of this impact has yet to be studied thoroughly because of the secrecy surrounding the tests.
- The greatest threat to the future survival of wilderness communities in the South Pacific is indirect; global warming caused by years of emissions of greenhouse gases in EMDCs is resulting in rising sea levels. Few countries or communities in the South Pacific region have the financial resources to combat this threat.

References and further reading

Internet websites:

For general environmental impacts on the South Pacific try Pactok on:
HYPERLINK http://www.pactok.net.au/cat/cat.htm

For impacts of mining try The Mineral Policy Institute on:
HYPERLINK http://www.hydra.org.au/mpi/

For impacts upon forestry try the Gaia Forest Archives on:
HYPERLINK http://forests.org/

There are very few books on the South Pacific but some articles exist, e.g. *Geographical Magazine*, February 1997, and *New Internationalist*, June 1997 (the whole issue).

For tourism, identify its extent by contacting long-haul holiday companies such as Kuoni or Inspirations. Their brochures are found in most travel agents, while an investigation of travel advertisements at the back of broadsheet newspapers will identify companies which specialize in 'wilderness adventure' holidays. Cable and satellite television have good programmes on tourism and biodiversity, such as those on 'Discovery', the 'National Geographic' channel and the 'Travel' channel.

Managing threats to wilderness regions

Identifying pressures on wilderness regions

Chapters 2 and 3 have shown that both real and potential conflicts exist in wilderness areas as pressure to develop their resources grows. Global pressure groups have demanded that economic and political interests become more sensitive to the natural world, so that environments are considered as part of the decision-making process about how space is used. This chapter will show how tourism and other economic pressures have raised questions of conservation and preservation. It will consider how the threats to wilderness areas can and are being managed. It will focus upon:

- the Great (or Grand) Staircase region of Utah, where economic development threatens the environment
- how the emergence of ecotourism may offer alternatives to these threats
- how protection policies which have produced National Parks may need some rethinking in view of future demands for space.

▼ **Figure 4.1** Location of Utah within the USA, showing the Great Staircase region.

Development versus conservation – the debate about the Great Staircase region

Economic development places pressure upon environments. By contrast, conservation means to 'save', and therefore implies that economic development should either a) be prevented, or b) be carried out selectively so as not to spoil those parts of an area considered to be worth saving.

Tourism – probably the world's fastest growing economic activity – places its own pressures upon environments. When these are added to those from other human activities, the conflict between conservation and economic development may become intense. This is well illustrated in Utah, USA, (Figure 4.1) where the value of the Great Staircase wilderness region, shown in Figure 4.2, is disputed by the federal government, local politicians, environmental groups and the mining companies, Conoco and Andalex Resources Incorporated.

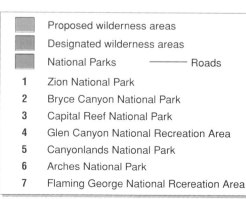

Proposed wilderness areas	
Designated wilderness areas	
National Parks	——— Roads

1 Zion National Park
2 Bryce Canyon National Park
3 Capital Reef National Park
4 Glen Canyon National Recreation Area
5 Canyonlands National Park
6 Arches National Park
7 Flaming George National Rcereation Area

In Utah, the Great Staircase region provides a challenge for environmental management for a number of reasons. Figure 4.2 shows how it is considered by some to be an important environment with dramatic wilderness quality. It is a huge semi-desert area of rugged sandstone cliffs and canyons. Among the canyons are two of the best-known in the USA – Zion and Bryce Canyon – and the Canyonlands National Park. Utah probably contains the largest area of remaining wilderness in the USA outside Alaska, and may itself be worthy of protection.

Under the 1964 Wilderness Act in the USA, this region was protected from further human invasion and development. However, Senators from Utah are now keen to open up some 9 million hectares in Utah for economic development, including parts of the Great Staircase. They claim that it is only a very small area within a vast wilderness, so the overall impact upon the landscape will be minimal, while the economic benefits to Utah would strongly outweigh environmental costs. Figure 4.3 tells the story in detail.

Blazing battle to keep the West wild

▲ **Figure 4.2** The Great Staircase region, Utah.

Ed Vulliamy on the race by Utah oilmen to strike it rich before Al Gore puts the wilderness off limits

The call of the coyote carries over the rim of the great cliffs that rise behind Kanab, Utah, a scrappy frontier town that has changed little in a century.

This landscape, sweet with the scent of juniper, was the last corner of America to be mapped and remains the country's most remote wilderness, a place of savage beauty.

The Great Staircase of Utah began forming 250 million years ago, when colliding land masses lifted the Colorado plateau and rivers gouged through the cliffs. The result is a wonderland of florid rock, natural bridges, immense canyons and three 'stairs', each 1,000 ft [300m] high.

Now it is at the centre of a bitter dispute that goes to the heart of American politics. On one side is the federal government, seeking to conserve what is left of the great American wilderness. On the other are mining companies and local interests determined to prevent it from doing so.

The conflict threatens to undermine Al Gore's dream of a 'green presidency' – when his time comes, as he hopes it will, at the end of Clinton's second term.

A year ago Clinton declared all 1.7 million acres [700 000 hectares] of the Great Staircase to be the United States' biggest 'National Monument'. For Utah, a state that has been scrapping against government authority ever since its inception, this was a provocative act. 'The mother of all land grabs,' said Utah's senator, Orrin Hatch. Effigies of the President were hung from lamp posts.

Clinton hoped that after a three-year review the government's conservationists, local political and business leaders and the citizenry could agree on the 'joint management' of the monument.

But the attempt to sabotage it has already begun, seeking to undermine the area's status, defined by the Great Wilderness Statute of 1964 as 'untramelled by man'.

High on the plateau, roads are being cut like scars. At the moment they lead nowhere, but county authorities argue that the roads mean this is not true 'wilderness'.

To prove the point, they are bulldozing the roads and up-grading old cattle-crossing tracks into county highways. These roads were the main threat to the Great Staircase – until Clinton caved in.

Four weeks ago, he announced that the Conoco oil company of Houston,

Texas, could begin exploratory drilling at the monument's heart. If it strikes lucky, it is authorised to extract.

The President insists that he is merely honouring a pledge to respect existing drilling rights – which Conoco had. But that hardly convinces environmentalists. It is the first time that a US government has allowed drilling in a national monument.

'The Interior Department is dangerously close to opening the barn door and shooing the horse out,' says Fran Hunt, of the Wilderness Society. 'This is not the kind of place you want to go to smell diesel fuel.' Scott Groene, of the South Utah Wilderness Alliance, adds: 'If the Government says it's OK to drill now, it means this place has crumbled and the monument is meaningless. if they find no oil, then the damage is just about containable. If they find it – well, we've got an oilfield.'

The alliance has been the most tenacious of the 60 groups that secured the designation of the Staircase and have campaigned to retain it.

'It's an increasingly rare thing in this country, a big block of undeveloped land,' says Groene. 'We have a responsibility to hand future generations some places that haven't been used up.'

Groene is most concerned about the precedents that striking oil would set – oil is but a minor richness of this majesty of nature. The greatest treasure is coal. Seven billion tons of high-energy, clean-burning coal – one of America's largest deposits.

Coal mining is an attractive alternative for Utah, whose lumber and ranching industries have fallen on hard times. The coal within the Great Staircase has been left alone for lack of any means to transport it and a terminal from which to ship it. But the growth of a vast coal terminal at Los Angeles has the potential to change all that.

The Andalex Resources Inc. mining company was part of the consortium that built the LA terminal. It bought the mining rights for the Great Staircase 10 years ago and has devised a 50-year plan to extract the coal.

Local politicians say the coal from one small area could earn about $3 billion (£1,85 bn) in taxes for the state of Utah, and $1 million for the county. Andalex is talking about 1,000 jobs in a county of 6,000 people. 'One canyon looks much like another,' says Kane County commissioner, Joe Judd. The area is so dry, says Andalex project manager David Shaver, that 'even the snakes shun it'. Shaver says the damage would be akin to 'a frisbee on a football field' – a claim hotly challenged by government scientists.

There is another leg to the argument against industrial development: tourism. Visitors to Utah's canyon parks have increased by 300 per cent in the past decade.

Roger Holland, a Kanab councilman (and mining consultant), believes that tourism is 'more trouble than it's worth. Visitors put pressure on water, sewerage, services.'

Groene argues: All this is just crazy. What is it that they are trying to preserve? The history of oil and gas drilling in arid lands? We already have enough of that – in slag heaps and abandoned drill sites.'

The reality, says Jim Baca, former director of the federal Bureau of Land Management, is 'that the blue-collar jobs that once co-existed with tourism are largely gone. It's hard stuff for people to accept, but their way of life is ending. They think they have a right to exist forever in a nineteenth century economy and be subsidised to do it. There's no sense in ripping up these last wild areas, no sense at all.'

▲ **Figure 4.3** From *The Observer,* 12 October 1997.

▼ **Figure 4.4** The ecosystem of Utah's semi-desert.

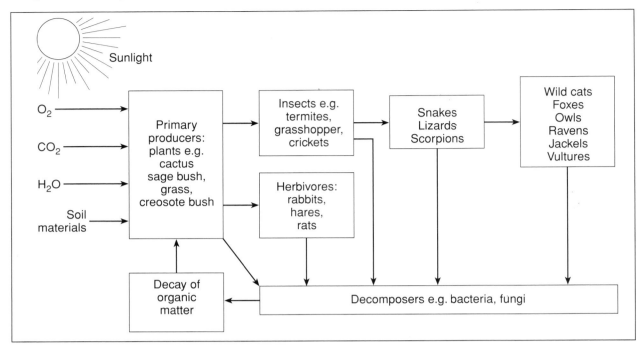

The concept of 'sustainable development'

The word 'development' means change. The study of development means rather more – it generally refers to the process of improving quality of life. This may include wealth, health, peace, justice, freedom and environmental quality. The concept of sustainable development means to meet 'the needs of the present without compromising the ability of future generations to meet their own needs' (Brundtland 1987/88). This means that whatever resources we use should be managed in such a way that they are allowed to regenerate faster than the levels at which they are being exploited – hence the meaning of the word 'sustainable'.

The concept of sustainability is used in many countries, in order to attempt to conserve areas considered worthy of protection. Effective management strategies therefore require a balance between three factors:

1 a thorough understanding of the natural ecosystem
2 an understanding of the demand for its resources
3 an evaluation of the extent to which the concept of sustainability can be applied.

This requires that we fully understand nature and how it is being used and/or exploited so that policies can be developed to manage resources in a sustainable way. Environmentally sustainable development usually focuses on the cliché 'long-term need' rather than 'short-term greed'.

Fundamental to this process is a thorough understanding of the structure and functioning of the ecosystem (see Figure 4.4). In addition, it is also necessary to understand the societies involved and how they perceive their need for resources, so a profitable relationship can exist with the environment without destroying it. The concept of 'use–renewal' (shown in Figure 4.5) can be applied to ecosystems. If rates of use exceed rates of recovery, environmental degradation will occur. This is difficult to measure, however, especially if rates of recovery are affected by rates of use. In managing wilderness regions, rates of use may be minimal but rates of recovery may be even less, particularly where ecosystems are very fragile.

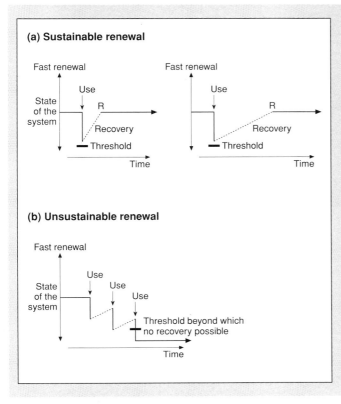

(a) Sustainable renewal

(b) Unsustainable renewal

◀ **Figure 4.5** Sustainable 'use–renewal'. (a) In a sustainable system, successive use will not reoccur until recovery has taken place, shown as point 'R'. Recovery rates vary depending upon the ecosystem. (b) Where rates of use exceed recovery rates, degradation occurs, and a threshold is reached beyond which recovery is not possible. (Source: adapted from Trudgill, *Geography Review*, Philip Allan Publishers Ltd, 1992.)

Any management has to address the needs of two populations – the indigenous population and the wider society within a country. Sometimes, a third population – in other countries – may be important, as the global resistance to French nuclear testing in the South Pacific showed. In addition, it needs to comply with international standards and awareness of global sustainable development. Current management initiatives must not prejudice the future, and sustainable management allows a site to be managed in such a way that it will leave it in good if not better environmental condition than when the management began.

Can the management of the Great Staircase be sustainable?

Study Figures 4.3, 4.4 and 4.5 and the theory box on sustainable development.

1 a) Identify the main players in the debate about the Great Staircase in Utah.

   b) Devise a conflict matrix (Figure 3.13 on page 33) to show different conflicts.

   c) Assess the strength of the conflict. Is it based on social, economic or environmental interests?

2 What do you consider to be the key characteristics of sustainable development in terms of the Great Staircase landscape?

3 Should Senators elected by people to represent the state of Utah be conserving its remaining wilderness areas, or developing the economic contribution that these areas can make to the nation? Assess the strength of arguments on both sides.

Ecotourism in wilderness regions

The example of Utah illustrates some of the pressures faced by one wilderness region. In addition to pressures from mining, Figure 4.5 shows how protection is required simply in order to manage the increase in the number of visitors. Both within and outside the USA, increasing awareness of and access to wilderness regions has made them very popular. Awareness of wilderness areas, and interest in remote environments, has led to the emergence of ecotourism; that is, tourism which attempts to develop sustainably, without destroying the very resource that people come to visit.

Ecotourism is a major economic activity in itself. Even at the end of the 1980s, World Wide Fund for Nature showed that, of the US $55 billion earned by ELDCs through tourism, about US $12 billion came from ecotourism. People are also aware that tourism may present costs in conserving areas that they visit. In the late 1990s, research has shown how, in the USA, 7 million tourists are willing to pay between US $2000 and US $3000 for an ecotour.

▶ **Figure 4.6** Advertisements for ecotours.

1 On a world map, label the destinations offered in the advertisements in Figure 4.6. Are their locations similar in any way?

2 What attractions do these types of holiday offer that would make you choose to visit a harsh, remote wilderness region? To what extent do these attractions appeal to your own age group? Carry out a survey in your college or school to assess the desirability of the destinations shown.

Antarctica – beyond its true capacity?

Even remote destinations like Antarctica are attracting increasing numbers of ecotourists. Figure 4.7 shows numbers of visitors to Antarctica between 1980 and 1992/3; by 1997, the number of visitors had grown further to 8000, some paying as much as US $20 000 for the experience. Though far from the numbers who visit mass tourist destinations each year (in the UK, Cornwall receives something like 300 000 visitors during August alone), the introduction of tourism is nonetheless significant. How far is Antarctica able to cope with this influx, and should numbers continue to rise?

This raises the issue of capacity of tourist sites or destinations, beyond which irreversible damage may be done. In environmentally sensitive locations, among which wilderness areas are included, a measure of carrying capacity is essential. Carrying capacity refers to the number of people which can be accommodated sustainably. Prosser (*Managing Environmental Systems*, Nelson, 1995) identifies four elements in this:

▼ **Figure 4.7** Visitor numbers to Antarctica.

Year	By sea	By air	Total
1980/81	855	Unknown	855
1981/82	1441	*	1441
1982/83	719	2	721
1983/84	834	265	1099
1984/85	544	92	636
1985/86	631	151	782
1986/87	1797	30	1827
1987/88	2782	244	3026
1988/89	3146	370	3516
1989/90	2460	121	2581
1990/91	4698	144	4842
1991/92	5270	153	5423
1992/93	5526	168	5694
Total	**30 703**	**1740**	**32 443**
* Figure includes tourists arriving by sea and by air.			

- physical capacity – the maximum number of visitors that can be accommodated by site facilities
- ecological capacity – the maximum level of use which can occur before irreversible damage is done to the ecosystem
- economic capacity – the maximum number of visitors that can co-exist with other economic activities within the area, such as forestry or farming
- perceptual capacity – the maximum recreational use beyond which the quality of recreational experience would decline.

By definition ecotourism cannot exceed these boundaries. However, carrying capacity varies. Antarctica is clearly able to accommodate fewer people than, for instance, a wilderness region of the USA, because accessibility for people and services is restricted by the physical geography of the continent.

▼ **Figure 4.8** From *The Independent*, 5 November 1997.

Travel industry seeks to open up last great wilderness

Antarctica, the world's last unexplored continent, may also be about to become its next frontier for tourism: Environmentalists fear for its delicate ecosystem. Our correspondent in Sydney assesses the risks.

By Robert Milliken

In the biggest reassessment of its operations in Antarctica since the end of the Cold War, Australia has proposed closing two if its three research bases on the continent and turning them into summer bases for adventure tourists. Britain, New Zealand and Russia already allow tourists to visit Antarctica, but only by ship. There are occasional tourist flights over the continent from Australia and new Zealand, but up to now no tourists have been allowed to camp there because of fears for the security of penguin rookeries and other features of Antarctica's delicate ecosystem.

Now, Australia's Antarctic science advisory committee, a government body, has recommended that Australia should consolidate the scientific research done at its Casey and Mawson bases at the third base, Davis, and set up a regular air link between Australia and the Davis base, leasing the other two to other countries or allowing tourists to go there on strictly controlled expeditions.

Australia is one of seven countries with territorial claims to Antarctica, with Argentina, Britain, Chile, France, New Zealand and Norway.

The Australian claim covers about 43 per cent of the continent, almost as much as Australia itself. Its operations in Antarctica reflect the Cold War era, when countries that signed the Antarctic Treaty in 1959 were keen to protect their patches from encroachment by others.

But this has been an expensive business. Australia's three bases are about 1000 km apart from each other, each with its own transport system and infrastructure. These logistics consume two-thirds of Canberra's Antarctic budget of about A$60 m (£26 m) a year, leaving only one-third for the bases' real purpose: research on world climate change, sea life, glaciers, space physics and human impact on Antarctica itself over the 100 years since a British expedition from Australia was the first to spend a winter on the continent in 1898-99.

The committee's report, Australia's Antarctic Programme Beyond 2000, argues that the Cold War mentality should give way to a more co-operative approach, which, with Australia sharing logistics and supply lines with neighbouring Antarctic countries, would leave more money for research. The Australian government is likely to accept the recommendations.

The report's recommendation on increasing access for tourism is likely to be controversial, especially with Greenpeace and other environmental groups. It sits oddly with Australia's attitude eight years ago, when it opposed, on environmental grounds, an international convention allowing Antarctica to be opened up to minerals exploration for the first time.

Mining was forbidden under the 1959 Antarctic Treaty, which also banned military operations on the continent.

Australian officials are stressing that the proposal is a response to growing demand among tourist operators to visit Antarctica, and the need to meet such pressure with strict environmental controls.

Greenpeace opposes Britain and the United States landing aircraft in Antarctica, and would raise an outcry if Australia proposed adding an airstrip of its own.

The continent remains one of the world's last wonders for scientists and visitors alike. Its ice, in which fossils of apes resembling humans have been found, comprises more than two-thirds of the world's fresh water. Layers of its unmelted snow date back 1 million years. Its glaciers are populated by seals and penguins.

Underneath all this are thought to lie potential riches in the form of iron ore, coal, uranium and oil which could be the flashpoint for environmental battles in years to come.

As the Australian government contemplates what to do about its report, an Australian team of three men will embark today on the third day of an expedition to be the first Australians to walk unassisted 1,400 km to the South Pole.

▼ **Figure 4.9** Antarctic code of conduct for visitors, and the threats Antarctica faces. From *Antarctic Alternatives – Exploring Management Issues,* February 1995.

Code of conduct

1 Maintain a distance of at least 5-6 metres from penguins, nesting birds and crawling (or true) seals, and 15 metres from fur seals. Most of the Antarctic species exhibit a lack of fear which allows you to approach closely: however, please remember that the austral summer is a time for courting, mating, nesting and rearing young. If you approach the animals or birds too closely you may startle and disturb them sufficiently that they will abandon the nesting site, leaving eggs or chicks vulnerable to predators. And even from the recommended distance you will be able to obtain fantastic photographs.

You should also remember that wild animals, especially seals, are extremely sensitive to movement and a person's height above the ground in relation to their size. Approach wildlife slowly when preparing to take photographs. And it is important to remember that your photography is not over when the shutter clicks – make your retreat from the subject in the same way you approach. The key point to remember is not to cause the animals any distress. You should be careful to avoid altering their natural behaviour.

2 Be alert while you are ashore! Watch your step in order not to stumble upon an aggressive fur seal or a nesting bird that is unaware of your presence. And pay attention to the behaviour of flying birds, as well as those on the ground. For example when a tern or skua becomes excited or agitated and starts dive-bombing you, it is a good indication that you are walking too close to its nest, though you may not have spotted it.

3 Do not get between a marine animal and its path to the water nor between a parent and its young. Never surround a single animal, nor a group of animals and always leave them room to retreat. Animals always have the right-of-way!

4 Be aware of the periphery of a rookery or seal colony and remain outside it.

5 Do not touch the wildlife. The bond between parent and young can be disrupted and the survival of the young jeopardised.

6 Never harass wildlife for the sake of photography. Our intention is to observe wildlife in its natural state.

7 Keep all noise to a minimum in order not to stress the animals.

8 Avoid walking on, stepping on, or damaging the fragile mosses and lichens. Regeneration is extremely slow and the scars from human damage last for decades.

9 Take away only memories and photographs. Do not remove anything, not even rocks or limpet shells. This includes historical evidence of man's presence in Antarctica, such as whalebones seen at some sites, which resulted from the whaling industry's activities.

10 Return all litter to the ship for proper disposal. This includes litter of all types, such as film containers, wrappers, cigarette butts and tissues. Garbage takes decades to break down in this harsh environment.

11 Do not bring food of any kind ashore.

12 Do not enter buildings at the research stations unless invited to do so. Remember that scientific research is going on and any intrusion could affect the scientists' data. Be respectful of their work.

13 Historic huts can only be entered when accompanied by a specifically-designated government representative or properly authorised ship's leader.

14 Never smoke near wooden buildings or refuge huts. Fire is the greatest hazard in Antarctica! The wood is generally very dry and can easily catch fire, winds are usually prevalent and firefighting equipment is not readily available. Please return any cigarette butts to the ship for disposal.

15 When ashore, stay with the group and/or one of the ship's leaders. For your own safety, do not wander off on your own.

16 Listen to the expedition leaders, lecturers and naturalists. They are experienced and knowledgeable about Antarctica.

Source: Society Expeditions

The threats

Quotes

'Scientists worry that tourists, whose numbers are approaching 10,000 a year, pose a threat to the ecosystem.' (The Herald, October 8, 1990)

'Tourism could affect Antarctica more than mining, MP warns.' (The Age, June 18, 1990)

'Australian entrepreneurs propose Project Oasis – a runway for 747s, a five-storey hotel and a hovercraft dock.'. (The Herald, October 8, 1990)

'So many boats cruise along the peninsula between November and March that it has been dubbed the Antarctic Riviera.' (Time Magazine, January 15, 1990)

'Chile has opened a hotel near its base. Antarctic activities include hiking, mountain climbing, dog sledding, camping and skiing.' (Time Magazine, January 15, 1990)

'One witness indicated that his project had a market potential of 16,000 persons a year.' (Tourism in Antarctica)

'Last year (1989), the first commercial flights landed at the South Pole.' (The Herald, October 8, 1990)

'We had been warned that a dropped orange peel would be still free of decomposition two years later.' (Antarctica: A Traveller's Tale)

Read Figures 4.7–4.9.

1 How far does it seem as though Prosser's ideas about capacity (physical, ecological, economic and perceptual) are being applied in Antarctica?

2 What do you see as the future threats to Antarctica, if tourism continues to increase?

With increasing tourism to wilderness areas, is it possible to ensure minimal impact on the environment, even through ecotourism? 'Take only photographs, leave only footprints' is perhaps the first rule of ecotourism. Environmentalist Bernadette Vallely (in her book *1001 Ways to Save the Planet*) lists 41 ways to act sustainably while on holiday. These include advice on a variety of aspects, from how to approach whales or scarce deer, to trekking and camping. To increase awareness among ecotourists, and reduce their environmental impact, various codes and practices often accompany the itinerary and air tickets – an example is shown in Figure 4.9. Although these are usually written by tour operators, in Nepal official codes are also found on the back of travel tickets and menus in trekking lodges.

Does ecotourism work?

One difficulty with ecotourism is that it means different things to different parties. In its purest sense, it is an industry which claims to make a low impact on the environment and local culture, while helping to generate money and employment, and promote conservation of wildlife and vegetation. It aims to provide tourists with an authentic experience of natural environments, or societies and their cultures. However, it largely reflects Western ideas about environmental conservation. So does ecotourism work?

An ecosystem functions as a complex open system with inputs, throughputs, stores and outputs. Each component is interdependent, and a change to one will lead to change in another. Tourists impose a changed set of inputs to an ecosystem which impact upon the way it functions. All ecosystems have built in feedback mechanisms to enable them to adjust to change or disturbance, a balance known as dynamic equilibrium. Once a critical threshold is reached, the ecosystem cannot survive. Hence the potential threat posed by tourism.

▶ **Figure 4.10** Systems diagram of an ecosystem (source: P. J. Gersmehl, 'Antarctica Alternative Biography', *Annals of the Association of American Geographers*, vol. 66, 1976).

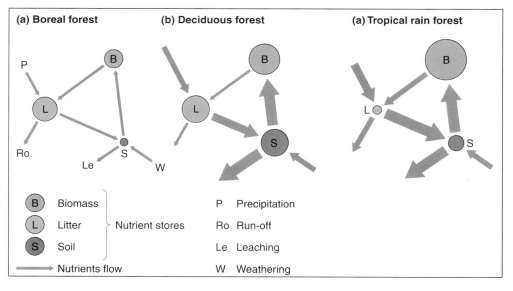

(a) Boreal forest   (b) Deciduous forest   (a) Tropical rain forest

B	Biomass		P	Precipitation
L	Litter	Nutrient stores	Ro	Run-off
S	Soil		Le	Leaching
→	Nutrients flow		W	Weathering

1 Describe specific ways in which tourism will affect the different components of an ecosystem (Figure 4.10). Consider:
   a) where tourists stay
   b) how they travel
   c) what and where they eat.

2 Try to classify your points into positive and negative, short-term and long-term.

Ecotourism in ELDCs

Many ELDCs envisage that tourism will provide them with much-needed hard currency, so they market their natural beauty spots in a big way. Tourism, however, is an environmentally-dependent industry and development comes at a price. No matter how aware tourists are, the sheer number of visitors to a fragile environmental area can lead to severe environmental degradation and disruption of local cultures. Ownership is also problematic, since many overseas developers purchase land and take large shares of profits.

Managing pressures upon Mount Everest

One success in recent years has been the 'clean-up' of the area around Mount Everest (Figure 4.11). Known as the Sagarmatha National Park, it is designated internationally as a World Heritage Site. It is situated in the north-east of Nepal and has long attracted trekkers and mountaineers with its spectacular scenery, hospitable Sherpa villages, Buddhist monasteries and Everest, the world's highest mountain, which is known to the Nepalese as Sagarmatha.

Some 16 000 foreign trekkers and mountain climbers visited Sagarmatha in 1994. The attractions are immense. During the peak climbing season, many expeditions camp at the Everest base. Each expedition can carry as much as 3600 kilos of supplies, most of which is discarded as rubbish. Walking trails and camping grounds had become littered with rubbish – sweet wrappers, film cartons or food cans – while improper disposal of human waste was causing ecological and health threats. Equally seriously, demand for scarce fuelwood from both the foreign visitors and the 3000 resident Sherpas has led to deforestation.

With WWF assistance, local villagers have formed a committee – the Sagarmatha Pollution Control Committee (SPCC) – which attempts to:

- prevent and control pollution in Sagarmatha
- strengthen reforestation efforts
- protect the park's remaining forests.

It includes representatives and advisers from local voluntary clubs, village development councils, and the warden of the Sagarmatha National Park. A deposit system has introduced charges, based on weight of equipment and supplies brought into the park, to encourage visitors to bring back as much as possible at the end of their trip. All charges are used to finance the 'clean-up' operation.

▼ **Figure 4.11** Nepal, showing the location of Mount Everest and the Annapurna Conservation Area Project. In Nepal, 13.8 per cent of the country's land surface totalling 20 238 square kilometres, is protected.

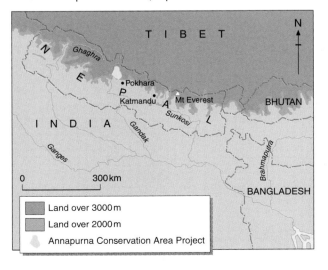

The SPCC has tried different methods to manage human waste, such as incinerators and composting. Support for better waste management from the community and visitors is sought through training workshops and public education. In addition, brochures and posters in the visitor centres in Lukla and Namche try to educate people.

The success of the SPCC has led to the enforcement of regulations by the Ministry of Tourism and Civil Aviation, which limit numbers of expeditions to Everest. Since 1993, the SPCC has received funds from the Ministry, who have committed money to environmental improvement. The SPCC has gained momentum in the 1990s, and has expanded its activities to include community services, environmental protection, tourism development and cultural preservation.

The Annapurna region in western Nepal

▼ Figure 4.12 From *The Royal Geographical Magazine,* June 1997.

A SPIRITUAL JOURNEY

THE ANNAPURNA CIRCUIT HAS A GREAT DEAL TO OFFER IN TERMS OF SCENIC MAGNIFICENCE AND HOSPITALITY. BUT AS ANDREW STEVENSON DISCOVERED, THE FUTURE OF A LARGE SECTION OF THIS SUSTAINABLY MANAGED TREKKING ROUTE NOW HANGS IN THE BALANCE

It is the bhaatis situated every few hours along the trail and the friendly people running them that help make this Nepal's most popular trekking route.

Tourism revenue in Nepal is second only to foreign aid income, and an estimated 40,000 trekkers visit some part of the Annapurna range every year.

Yet with the popularity of this region comes intense ecological pressures. In an area with no electricity and little infrastructure, the sheer volume of tourists places a tremendous burden on the environment. More than 95 per cent of Nepal's energy requirements are met by the burning of wood, and for many years this meant indiscriminate felling of trees. The ultimate casualty has been Nepal's rhododendron forests. Until recently, as much as three per cent of the country's total area (about 400,000 hectares) was being cleared annually.

It was not before time, therefore, that the Annapurna Conservation Area Project (ACAP) was established in 1986. Unlike many other national parks worldwide, the 4,633 square kilometre conservation area does not exclude human habitation. Far from being displaced, the needs of the local people are integral to the project. Although there was some initial scepticism when the Nepalese government gazetted the Annapurnas as a park, local people have since come to realise that they have a lot to gain from the situation. The traditional method of managing Nepal's forests, known as rititihiti, balanced cutting and growth.

However, the practice died out some 50 years ago, when the land was nationalised. In theory, forest cutting was monitored on behalf of the government by a sparsely distributed and non-local police force. But decades of destruction ensued; not just indiscriminate tree-felling, but also the large-scale poaching of forest animals.

In the eleven years since the formation of the ACAP, however, the responsibility for managing forests and wildlife has been handed back to villagers. The forests are once again communally controlled and distributed according to family requirements. If someone is caught cutting down a tree without permission or poaching an animal, villagers themselves levy fines, through village committees, and ensure that they are paid. It is not easy to get away with illegally using natural resources in a small, tightly-knit village community.

A locally-controlled non-governmental organisation, ACAP is funded by the fees paid by trekkers passing through the Annapurnas. It has devised a multitude of simple fuel-saving devices, including solar-heated showers, and runs health-related workshops for local people. Themes for workshops include hygiene (the necessity of boiling water, for example, or digging latrines) and the importance of using flues to exhaust cooking ovens. Flues prevent buildings filling up with smoke, which is a major contributor to one of the biggest health problems in the region, tuberculosis.

Tourism is something of a necessary evil for people living in the Himalayas. ACAP helps them to cope with the onslaught of trekkers, providing special courses on how to cater to their needs. Word soon spreads among trekkers as to which lodges provide the best service. As long as there are trekkers demanding clean toilets, boiled or filtered drinking water and smokeless ovens, there is an economic incentive for locals to offer them. However, this will not happen overnight.

▲ **Figure 4.13** Trekking is popular in the Annapurna sanctuary.

The effects of tourism extend beyond the Annapurna region's natural resources; trekkers have introduced Western ideas and values that have had an undeniable impact on young people. Many have been so 'Westernised' that they consider local traditions backward. ACAP runs an innovative programme to encourage young people, as well as trekkers, to appreciate traditional ways, and to instill a sense of pride in the traditional lifestyle, costumes and dance.

Today, more than a decade since its formation, ACAP can be seen to be at the cutting edge of nature conservation and 'ecotourism'. It adopts a multiple land-use approach to natural resource management, combining environmental protection with sustainable grassroots community development. It has successfully empowered local people with skills and knowledge. With success, however, comes expansion, and ACAP's greatest challenge will be to handle an ever-growing workload.

It is easy to become jaded about development work, yet here is a project showing promise, based on its heady success. But plans to construct a new road up the Kali Gandaki make a mockery of all the environmentally and culturally sensitive issues raised. Within years, ACAP's success will be wiped out by an infrastructure project, funded by the Chinese, which will cost far more in environmental terms than any foreseen economic benefit.

ACAP cannot prevent the road being built, explains Dr Chandra Gurung, who was until recently the project's director. For political reasons, he is not in a position even to hint at lobbying against it. It depends, he agrees, on the will of the people: 'They must decide.'

Only 7,000 to 8,000 people reside there permanently, but an estimated 15,000 will be affected by the road. 'If you live in a remote area, you are entitled to certain government benefits. Many people actually live in Pokhara, unofficially, and commute to their remote villages as the need arises. These people would clearly like to see the road built.'

Without question though, the road will destroy the natural beauty of the region. The balance of the delicate ecosystem of the Kali Gandaki, and the vulnerable culture of its diverse peoples, will be radically changed. Do the Kali Gandaki inhabitants know this? If they knew what we know, what Nirmila knows having spent six months in the US, would they accept the prospect of a road and all its implications so unquestioningly?

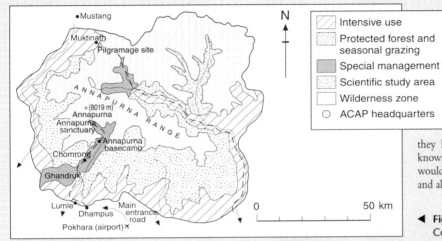

▲ **Figure 4.14** The Annapurna Conservation Area Project.

The spectacular mountain wilderness of the Annapurna region in western Nepal (Figures 4.12–4.14) has long attracted the more adventurous tourist. In 1991, 270 000 tourists visited Nepal; 70 000 were trekkers, 55 per cent of these heading for the Annapurna region.

Look at Figures 4.12–4.14.

1 How sustainable does tourism seem to be in Annapurna? Justify your answer.

2 Which do you consider to offer the best role model for ecotourism – the Annapurna region, Sagarmatha or Antarctica? Explain your choice.

3 Can ecotourism really balance economic development and conservation? What seem to be the main problems in achieving this balance?

4 In groups of three or four, discuss how far you agree with the following statements. Present your ideas to the rest of the class.

● 'Ecotourism is simply tourism for the wealthy.'

● 'By preserving regions through ecotourism, we are effectively locking them into a state of under-development. Only the mass tourist market can bring in the kind of income that most ELDCs need.'

Protecting for the future – the concept of National Parks

Since the ecotourist is continually searching for new experiences, tour operators are forced to constantly look for new areas to develop and the wilderness areas are under increasing threat. Three principles of sustainable tourism were established by the UK Government's Tourism and the Environment Task Force in May 1991:

1 The environment has an intrinsic value which outweighs its value as a tourism asset. Its enjoyment for future generations and its long-term survival must not be prejudiced by short-term considerations.
2 Tourism should be recognized as a positive activity with the potential to benefit the community and the place, as well as the visitor.
3 The relationship between tourism and the environment must be managed so that it is stable and long-term. Tourism must not be allowed to damage the resource, prejudice its future enjoyment or bring unacceptable impacts.

One way of managing these policies is to protect areas by defining them as National Parks. Some 5000 areas are protected globally as National Parks and reserves, covering 3 per cent of the Earth's surface. This percentage will be doubled by the end of the next century if conservationists win support. National Parks have moved from a national concept, used in establishing areas for protection in the early twentieth century, to a global concept which is increasingly important in ELDCs as a means of protecting rare habitats. National Parks are defined by the IUCNNR (International Union for the Conservation of Nature and Natural Resources) 1969 as relatively large areas where:

- ecosystems are not materially altered by human exploitation and occupation, where plant and animal species, geomorphological sites and habitats are of scientific, educative and recreational interest, or which contain a natural landscape of great beauty
- the highest authority of the country has tried to prevent or eliminate as soon as possible any exploitation or occupation, and to enforce the respect of landscape features which have led to its establishment
- visitors are allowed to enter, under special conditions, for inspirational, cultural and recreational purposes.

The IUCNNR definition is not applicable to UK National Parks, since the parks are nearly all settled, farmed and exploited, and are largely in private ownership. In some parks there is intense conflict between those hired to protect the wildlife and those asserting their right to gain a living from the land. Globally, many countries have established state-owned lands which are protected from extensive economic development. This section will look at how land is protected in the USA, and evaluate how well policies act to conserve such areas.

Protecting land in the USA

The first area to be established as a National Park in the USA was in 1872 at Yellowstone. In August 1916, President Woodrow Wilson signed the USA National Park Service Act creating 36 National Parks under a single federal (or national) agency 'to conserve the scenery and the natural and historic objects and the wildlife therein, and to provide for the enjoyment of the same in such manner, and by such means as will leave them unimpaired for the enjoyment of future generations'. Described by former British ambassador to the USA, James Bryce, as 'the best idea America ever had', National Parks in the USA today cover over 30 million hectares in 357 sites which include some of the last natural refuges for the USA's plant and animal species. These are found in areas as varied as the Grand Canyon (Figure 4.15) in the western USA, and the Appalachian mountain region in the east. To appreciate the sheer extent of some areas, read Bill Bryson's *A walk in the woods* about the Appalachian trail, which is both readable and very funny.

The National Park Service with some 34 million hectares supervises 11 per cent of public lands. With 54 National Parks covering over 20 million hectares the Park Service offers outdoor activities to the increasing urban population. Under the National Park Service natural resources are protected but hunting, fishing and extraction of minerals and fuels are permitted.

Management of wilderness lands within the USA is complicated by the fact that there are a variety of federal departments whose responsibility it is to manage areas of land. The Forest Service for example, under the Department of Agriculture, covers over 80 million hectares with 155 national forests comprising 25 per cent of public lands, mostly in the mountainous west and Alaska. They frequently have to compromise between competing demands of logging, grazing, mining, watershed protection and recreation.

What pressures face National Parks in the USA?

Figure 4.16 shows how this system is under enormous strain. In 1960 the Park Service managed 187 sites covering over 10 million hectares. This has since trebled in area, including the addition of more than 16 million hectares of Alaska wilderness in 1980. Budgets have not kept pace with public use and land acquisitions, and the service has to

▲ **Figure 4.15** The Grand Canyon – one of the USA's most spectacular National Parks.

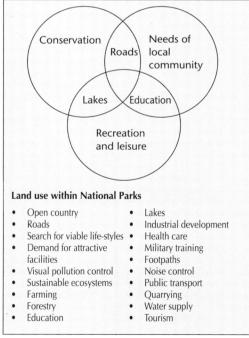

Land use within National Parks

- Open country
- Roads
- Search for viable life-styles
- Demand for attractive facilities
- Visual pollution control
- Sustainable ecosystems
- Farming
- Forestry
- Education

- Lakes
- Industrial development
- Health care
- Military training
- Footpaths
- Noise control
- Public transport
- Quarrying
- Water supply
- Tourism

▲ **Figure 4.16** Conflicts within National Parks (adapted from Smith and Smith, *Geofile*, January 1993).

choose between land maintenance, equipment repairs and staffing. As a result it relies on partnership with private land conservancies who buy and manage land as preserves, or hold them in trust until they can be acquired by the Park Service. Concerned citizens have also established the National Park Trust which is raising money to buy the private lands within the National Parks.

The concept of 'refuges'

Since the creation of the National Parks established the principle of putting wildlife first, over 500 federal refuges for wildlife have been created across the USA. A refuge is land set aside from economic development in order to provide habitats for wildlife. This measure takes control of land, protecting it from commercial interests, in order to provide space for future refuges as well as other forests and National Parks. About 90 per cent of wildlife refuges have been created from existing lands within national forests and ranges. Most of the money required to purchase them came from the Land and Water Conservation Agency in the 1960s or from revenue from off-shore drilling leases. The original purpose was not so much to conserve wildlife as to increase public space for outdoor recreation.

Each refuge is managed, and refuge managers set standards to ensure that all activities are compatible with wildlife. However, hunting dog trials, power boat racing, the use of beach buggies and other off-road vehicles all meet the standards, as do commercial fishing, cutting timber, hay-making and farming! It seems that some clarification is called for.

Attempts by the US Congress to define what is compatible with wildlife and what is not have met with no real success. According to surveys by the General Accounting Office and the Fish and Wildlife Service, the refuge system harbours 168 currently threatened or endangered species on one hand, while on the other 60 per cent of all refuges permit activities harmful to wildlife. The Fish and Wildlife Service has no control of the most harmful practices such as military activities and oil drilling.

1 Draw a Venn diagram like the one below. Classify the human activities which take place in refuges in the USA.

1 Social and economic
2 Economic and environmental
3 Environmental and social
4 All three

2 How do these activities conflict with the aims of wildlife refuges?

3 Form groups of three or four. The following suggestions are possible ways forward. Identify the merits and problems presented by each one:
a) Ban all activities which in some way threaten wildlife.
b) Ban all hunting, but permit sports and sporting outdoor activities such as power boat racing.

c) Permit farming, but prevent hunting and sporting outdoor activities such as power boat racing.

d) Provide limited permits to hunt, fish, shoot, etc. The limits would be set at levels at which wildlife would be able to maintain current populations.

e) Take no action and allow current practices to persist.

4 Which is your preferred option? How would you implement this option? Over what period? How would you enforce it, if enforcement were necessary?

The Arctic Wildlife Refuge

The Arctic Wildlife Refuge includes the eastern part of Alaska's Brooks Range and North Slope and the Yukon Delta, whose rivers and lakes are frozen for eight months of the year. The wildlife includes myriad birds, black bears, moose, wolverines, mink, musk oxen, bearded seals and beluga whales. These form the resource base for the Native American Yupik people who own 1.6 million hectares within the refuge boundaries which include most of the bird breeding grounds. Subsistence hunting and fishing privileges have been granted to the Yupik people, but despite subsistence levels, various geese species started to decline between the 1960s and 1980s through over-hunting. Talks were held between officials of Alaska and California, where the geese wintered. The Yupik agreed to halt egg gathering and midsummer hunting but insisted on the need to hunt in spring and autumn.

Hunting is permitted in over half of refuges in the USA, and brings about 1.6 million visitors per year. But hunters and fishermen are outnumbered four to one by visitors who come to watch and learn about the wildlife.

Trapping is also allowed in 207 refuges as a way of limiting problem species such as skunk that plunder bird nests, or muskrats that weaken dikes around ponds through tunnelling.

Denali National Park, USA

This National Park is the largest continuously protected ecosystem in the world and includes Mount McKinley, the highest peak on the North American continent at 6194 metres. It is located between Anchorage and Fairbanks and covers approximately 2.4 million hectares, nearly three times the area of Yellowstone National Park. Some 520 000 hectares are designated as National Preserve rather than a National Park, and hunting is permitted. Because of the park's potential as a site for ecological research, it was designated an International Biosphere Reserve in 1976. This designation provides a model for the management of multiple use reserves. The concept is simple: people are made part of the park or reserve. This makes local people stewards of the reserve, and also provides a method of generating income which should help protect the reserve from commercial exploitation.

Each preserve has a strictly controlled preserved area usually in the centre with zones of increasing use towards the boundary. The edge or buffer zone is designed to be used sustainably and people living there are considered to be the first line of defence against exploitative intruders. Many multiple use reserves are designed as a series of concentric rings with a strict reserve in the core or centre. The centre may be used for scientific research or nature tourism. Indigenous people living in low densities practising low impact land use may live in the buffer zone.

Denali faces several threats:

- a proposed 160-kilometre road or railroad that would run from the north-east corner to the Kantishna area in the heart of the park, cutting through pristine lands and reducing the corridor's suitability for wildlife
- mining in the Kantishna Hills
- the encroachment of developing tourist facilities and access on the south-east side of the park.

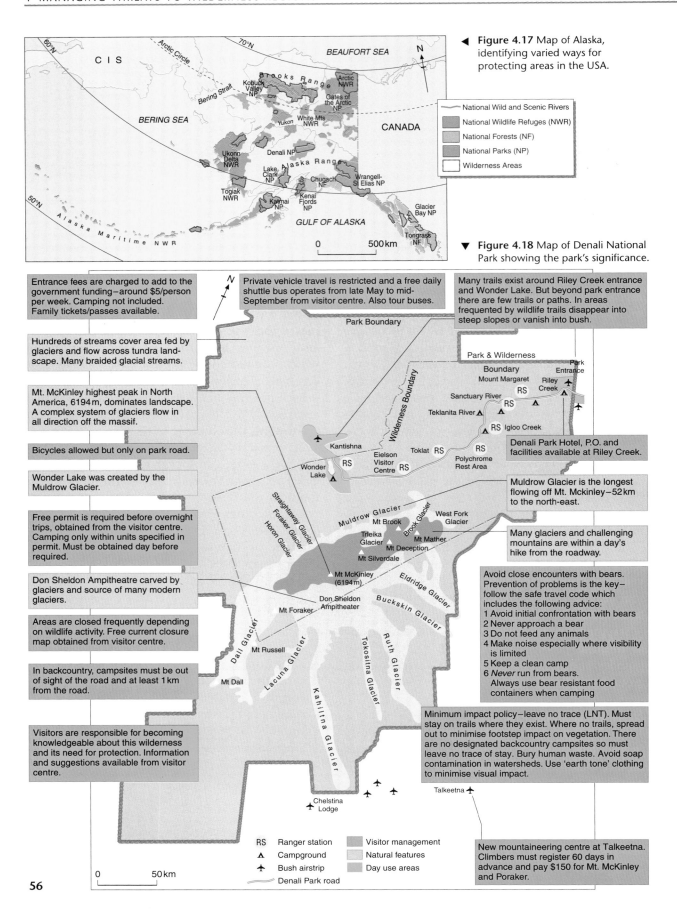

◀ **Figure 4.17** Map of Alaska, identifying varied ways for protecting areas in the USA.

Map legend:
- National Wild and Scenic Rivers
- National Wildlife Refuges (NWR)
- National Forests (NF)
- National Parks (NP)
- Wilderness Areas

▼ **Figure 4.18** Map of Denali National Park showing the park's significance.

Entrance fees are charged to add to the government funding—around $5/person per week. Camping not included. Family tickets/passes available.

Private vehicle travel is restricted and a free daily shuttle bus operates from late May to mid-September from visitor centre. Also tour buses.

Many trails exist around Riley Creek entrance and Wonder Lake. But beyond park entrance there are few trails or paths. In areas frequented by wildlife trails disappear into steep slopes or vanish into bush.

Hundreds of streams cover area fed by glaciers and flow across tundra landscape. Many braided glacial streams.

Mt. McKinley highest peak in North America, 6194 m, dominates landscape. A complex system of glaciers flow in all direction off the massif.

Bicycles allowed but only on park road.

Wonder Lake was created by the Muldrow Glacier.

Denali Park Hotel, P.O. and facilities available at Riley Creek.

Muldrow Glacier is the longest flowing off Mt. Mckinley—52 km to the north-east.

Free permit is required before overnight trips, obtained from the visitor centre. Camping only within units specified in permit. Must be obtained day before required.

Many glaciers and challenging mountains are within a day's hike from the roadway.

Don Sheldon Ampitheatre carved by glaciers and source of many modern glaciers.

Avoid close encounters with bears. Prevention of problems is the key—follow the safe travel code which includes the following advice:
1 Avoid initial confrontation with bears
2 Never approach a bear
3 Do not feed any animals
4 Make noise especially where visibility is limited
5 Keep a clean camp
6 Never run from bears.
  Always use bear resistant food containers when camping

Areas are closed frequently depending on wildlife activity. Free current closure map obtained from visitor centre.

In backcountry, campsites must be out of sight of the road and at least 1 km from the road.

Minimum impact policy—leave no trace (LNT). Must stay on trails where they exist. Where no trails, spread out to minimise footstep impact on vegetation. There are no designated backcountry campsites so must leave no trace of stay. Bury human waste. Avoid soap contamination in watersheds. Use 'earth tone' clothing to minimise visual impact.

Visitors are responsible for becoming knowledgeable about this wilderness and its need for protection. Information and suggestions available from visitor centre.

New mountaineering centre at Talkeetna. Climbers must register 60 days in advance and pay $150 for Mt. McKinley and Poraker.

Map legend:
- RS Ranger station
- ▲ Campground
- ✈ Bush airstrip
- ~~ Denali Park road
- Visitor management
- Natural features
- Day use areas

▼ **Figure 4.19** Purposes and significance of Denali National Park.

Denali National Park

PURPOSE

Preserve lands and waters for the benefit, use, education, and inspiration of present and future generations.

Preserve scenic and geological value associated with the natural landscapes.

Maintain wildlife habitats and species.

Preserve extensive, unaltered ecosystems in their natural state.

Protect resources related to subsistence needs.

Protect historic and archaelogical sites.

Preserve wilderness resource values and related recreational opportunities.

Maintain opportunities for scientific research in undisturbed ecosystems.

Provide opportunities for rural residents to engage in subsistence way of life.

Access and tourism: The park is the most popular visitor destination in Alaska. The railway links the park with Anchorage, Fairbanks, and the ports of Whittier and Seward. Also linked to two major package towns from Seattle. The George Parks Highway parallels the railway. Most park visitors want to travel the 145km road into the park. Park is marketed as a 'must do' adventure. The park road is therefore a significant visitor resource.

SIGNIFICANCE

International: UN biosphere reserve under 'Man and the Biosphere' programme because of subarctic ecosystem research potential.

Large protected area: Nearly 2.5 million hectares of spectacular variety of flora and fauna; over 800 000 hectares has had protected status since 1917. Largest continually protected area in the world. Excellent opportunity to study large-scale natural ecosystems in setting.

Mountains: Major portion of Alaska Range dominated by Mt McKinley.

Glaciers: A number of large, active glaciers some of the longest in North America, up to 72km long and 6.5km wide.

Wildlife: Originally established as a refuge for large mammals, e.g. Dall sheep, caribou, wolves, grizzly bear, moose, fox. These are often seen, especially north of Alaska Range. Population numbers fluctuate but nowhere else in North America can such concentrations of these large species be observed in their natural setting. Also significant for wildfowl.

Plantlife: Outstanding examples of subarctic plant communties. More than 650 species of flowering plants and extensive tundra plant life are adapted to these extreme conditions.

Air quality and scenic resources: Because of exceptional air quality and lack of city lights there are outstanding views and excellent night sky visibility in autumn and winter. On a clear day, Mt McKinley can be seen from Anchorage, more than 200km south.

Cultural resources: There are more than 180 known cultural sites and complexes within Denali's boundaries and this is probably a fraction of the total sites contained in the park. They include archaelogical and historic sites associated with Athabascan Indians, early explorers, mining history and early days of the park. Historic mining activity dates back to the early 1900's e.g. the Kantishna Hills.

Mountaineering: Mt McKinley is considered one of the world's premier summits. Also other peaks in the park offer outstanding climbing opportunities, e.g. Mt Foraker.

Wilderness recreation opportunities: Cross country hiking, back country camping and winter rowing possibilities are available. Very few trails exist so visitors can explore a park where evidence of human use is minimal to non-existent in contrast to most other US wilderness areas.

▼ **Figure 4.21** Extract from the Denali Strategic Plan.

Extracts from a summary of major issues with long-term goals for 2002

Issue	Objective/Strategy in 1995 Statement for Management (*progress since 1995 indicated in italics*)	Long-term goals for 2002 in Denali National Park Strategic Plan
Concessions management	Determine what concession services are necessary and appropriate and prepare a concessions management plan to document decisions made through the planning process. Establish controls and evaluate preferential rights of existing operators and other groups. When determined necessary and appropriate, issue prospectuses and select concessioner(s). Phase out inappropriate services if necessary.	By 2002, a commercial services component is completed as part of the winter use and backcountry management plans. This serves as a blueprint for identifying necessary and appropriate services to be provided by commercial operators on park lands. By 2002, the park's concessions management complies with existing law and policy (NPS—48), and assures effective operational review, timely evaluations, and annual financial analyses are completed to assess appropriate value and return (revenue) to the government. By 2002, current commercial services are provided under an appropriate authorizing document such as an Incidental Business Permit, or a Concessions Permit. Prospectuses resulting in executed concessions permits are issued for necessary and appropriate services that require managed growth. By 2002, a new concessions contract, implementing park goals for commercial activities in the entrance area and along the road corridor, is written and executed for transportation services and related activities.
Infrastructure/facilities management	Provide safe, reliable facilities and support utilities to adequately serve and protect park visitors and resources. Determine the type, number and location of facilities and the necessary infrastructure. Analyze the feasibility of locating administrative facilities and services outside the park boundary.	By 2002, at least 85% of visitors are satisfied with the availability, accesssibility, and quality of park facilities and services. By 2002, visitor and employee safety incidents are reduced by 10%.
Managing use (special regulations)	Ensure that there are adequate regulatory controls and authorities to protect park resources and preserve the visitor experience. Propose special regulations if needed to solve unique enforcement problems that cannot be managed through other techniques. (*The park has drafted a special regulations package that is being reviewed internally before initiating the public involvement process.*)	By 2002, resource damage resulting from human use is minimized through effective enforcement and mitigation programs. By 2002, regulations affecting road use and snowmachine use are implemented and enforced.
Solid waste and hazardous materials management	Minimize the annual volume of solid and hazardous waste generated by park operations and visitor use, and prevent adverse impacts to public health and park resources. Fully implement and enforce the park's hazardous waste management plan. Implement a comprehensive recycling program for the park. (*The park has continued to make progress toward these goals since 1995.*)	By 2002, 100% of the park's waste stream will be properly disposed of and, where practical disposal sources exist, all identified recyclable material will be recycled. The volume of hazardous materials generated by park operations will be reduced 10% from 1996 levels.

Parks and reserves are intended to be protected areas. However, conflict erupts mainly when people with competing interests and different values interact. This process can be useful and is a function of a dynamic society. Park managers face up to conflict to protect the natural environment. In conflict management, a mutually agreeable outcome is sought through a degree of compromise. All participants must feel that they have gained something in the process. The existence of conflict can actually be helpful in clarifying what people want.

Investigation of Denali National Park

The class should divide into two groups of roughly equal size. One should consider the Arctic Wildlife Refuge and the other Denali National Park.

1 For your area, carry out a SWOT analysis on the pressures facing it (SWOT stands for 'Strengths, Weaknesses, Opportunities and Threats'). You need to consider what and where the strengths, weaknesses, opportunities and threats for your area are, and the ways in which the area is managed.

2 Feed back your analysis to the other half of the class. Discuss these points:
   a) Do the strengths of the ways in which the area is managed outweigh the weaknesses?
   b) Do the opportunities offered to each area outbalance the threats?

3 What improvements can you suggest to the ways in which each of the areas is managed?

Looking to the future

Within the world's protected areas, the future may depend largely upon the effects of global warming. A global temperature rise of 1°C may cause a latitudinal shift in climate and vegetation zones of up to 100 kilometres. At present, National Parks and other forms of protection delimit safe areas for species, but if global climates change, plants and animals finding themselves in unsuitable new climates will be trapped, unable to migrate to new areas. Consider the management approaches which you have studied in this chapter, and evaluate their advantages and disadvantages.

It may be that a more flexible approach is required and that existing management strategies, combined with ever-increasing pressures from economic interests, may be insufficient. It could be that the key to success will be to establish an interlinked, global network of protected areas allowing species to migrate. Perhaps the future will call for 'corridors' or 'pathways' of new, additional protected land between each of the established areas. Alternatively, we could surrender protection of some wilderness areas, or decide that resource exploitation hàs simply gone too far.

▼ **Figure 4.22** Summary table of management techniques.

Technique	Definition	Examples
Protected areas: National Parks and National Forest Reserves	Conservation areas protected from human activity but allowing public access, under government management	• Denali National Park, USA • Grand Canyon, USA • Korup, Cameroon • North York Moors, UK
Protected areas: National Wildlife Refuge	Areas protected to provide habitat for migratory birds, big game and endangered species of all types	• Arctic North-West Region, USA
Protected areas: Biosphere Reserves	Designated to allow conservation and human activity in harmony through core and buffer zones	• South Pacific Biodiversity Programme
Protected areas: World Heritage Sites	Special status as exemplary stage of world's evolutionary or biological history or contains endangered species or large wildlife reserve	• Yellowstone, Yosemite and Redwood National Parks, USA • Galapagos Islands NP, Ecuador • Great Barrier Reef, Australia • Fiordland NP, New Zealand • Giant's Causeway/coast, UK
Buffer zones	Areas around a core region where economic activity is allowed to continue	• Annapurna Sanctuary region, Nepal
Ecotourism	Responsible tourism which is environmentally and culturally sensitive	• Annapurna and Sagarmatha, Nepal • Antarctica
International conventions	Aim to curb international trade in endangered species and set strict safeguards on species under less threat	• Convention on International Trade in Endangered Species of Flora and Fauna (1973)

Writing a conclusion

The purpose of a conclusion

The main purpose of a conclusion is to draw together the evidence from the case studies used in the essay to support or reject the main ideas. A conclusion should:

- refer back to the original question
- state how well the case studies/evidence used in the essay support the main ideas/generalizations, *or*
- state how well the case studies/evidence used in the essay reject the main ideas/generalizations, *or*
- provide a final judgement, which says that there is insufficient evidence to answer the essay title for definite, and which may therefore raise limitations and suggest improvements
- include a personal opinion, based on evidence
- be about 12–15 lines in length, or 120–150 words.

Figure 4.23 shows one student's conclusion to the essay title:

'With reference to one wilderness area you have studied, outline some of the potential and actual conflicts between development and conservation.'

▼ **Figure 4.23** Student's conclusion to the essay title

In conclusion, this essay illustrates a variety of threats to conservation in Utah. Despite the 1964 Wilderness Act in the USA, Utah Senators are keen to open up some of the state including part of the Great Staircase for economic development. Conoco are providing actual conflict through their drilling for oil, and the potential conflict is enormous if they are lucky.

The extraction of coal in Utah is also providing potential conflict between development and conservation. Vast coal reserves have currently been left as removal of coal from the area was difficult. However, with the development of a large coal terminal in Los Angeles and the mining rights owned by the same company, economic development of the coal industry in Utah is now more likely, increasing potential conflict. Technology, economics and politics have increased the pressure of development at the expense of conservation.

Therefore I think that although there is legislation in place to protect an area, the US Government's priorities have changed and as the economy weakens or more resources are needed, development is taking precedence over conservation.

1 a) Read the conclusion and identify its strengths and weaknesses.
   b) Compare your comments with those of someone else.

2 Using Figure 4.24, take on the role of the examiner and mark a copy of the conclusion. Annotate it with positive and negative comments.

3 Using the same essay title, write your own conclusion for this essay using a different wilderness region.

▼ **Figure 4.24** Essay marking scheme (EdExcel, January 1998.

Knowledge of concepts, issues and case studies:

8–7	Sound knowledge of case studies, concepts and issues; relevant and detailed case study(ies) information showing sound locational knowledge.
6–4	Satisfactory knowledge of case studies, issues and concepts; may lack location or precise detail and not always relevant selection; may lack depth and/or range at lower end.
3–1	Generalised knowledge with a lack of specific reference to case study(ies); knowledge of concepts and issues less clear and may be inappropriate to the question – considerable irrelevance.

Understanding of issues and concepts and their application:

10–7	Sound understanding of concepts, well applied case study(ies) with relevance to the answer, shows evidence of evaluative comment.
6–4	Satisfactory understanding with some relevant application of case study material; less evidence of ability to evaluate and knowledge not as well applied to understanding of the question. At lower end tends to be descriptive.
3–1	Weak understanding of concepts and issues with limited reference to relevant case study material. Focus descriptive rather than evaluative.

Skills:

7–6	Good use of language including appropriate geographical terminology. Coherent line of relevant argument showing evidence of planning and a logical structure. Possible use of relevant diagrams and cartographic techniques. Clarity of expression with high standard of accuracy in the use of punctuation, grammar and spelling.
5–4	Reasonable clarity and fluency of expression with some use of appropriate geographical terminology. Arguments are generally relevant with some evidence of planning and structure. Some use of illustrative material, accuracy in the use of punctuation, grammar and spelling.
3–1	Satisfactory clarity of expression of basic ideas but not always in a logical structure. Limited use of A Level geographical terminology with little evidence of planning and argument. Basic use of English but with mistakes.

Ideas for further study

1 Research a case study of a wilderness area of a rainforest ecosystem where development versus conservation issues occur. Identify the threats to the wilderness. How is each threat being managed, and by whom? To what extent are the indigenous people involved in decision-making?

2 In groups, research a National Park in an ELDC.
   a) Draw an annotated sketch map to show the location and wilderness qualities of the park.
   b) Outline the management plans of the park. How do the management plans compare with those of Denali?
   c) Prepare a short-term and long-term plan for your park. Identify indicators which you would use to measure success. Present your findings to the rest of the class.

Summary

- Conflict occurs at a variety of scales in wilderness regions, which may impinge on and reduce their quality.

- Various strategies have been adopted to protect different types of wilderness regions.
- National Parks and reserves are intended to be protected areas, but conflict frequently occurs between conservation and proposed development.
- Effective management of a wilderness region must a) meet the needs of local people and b) be sustainable.

References and further reading

Bill Bryson, *A walk in the woods*, Doubleday, 1997.

J. Chaffey, *Managing Environments in Britain and Ireland*, Hodder & Stoughton, 1997 (Chapter 3).

Bob Digby (ed.), *The Physical Environment*, Heinemann, 1995 (Chapter 3).

Robert Prosser, *Natural systems and human responses*, Nelson, 1992 (pp242–6).

Articles in *Geography Review, Geographical, New Scientist, Time*. For example: *Geographical*, November 1992, February 1995, June 1997; *Geography Review*, May 1996, January 1997, May 1997, May 1998.

The future of wilderness regions

Introduction

In this chapter you will consider the possible future for wilderness regions. As we have seen in Chapter 4, many wilderness areas are under threat from a variety of pressures, as their assets are valued by increasing numbers of interests. The nature of their resources varies, from natural beauty and remoteness (and hence their classification as a 'wilderness'), to forest and mineral resources, land of strategic importance (such as northern Alaska) and land for economic development in a world whose population is increasing at a net annual rate of 1.6 per cent.

A variety of management strategies which may be effective in restricting further economic development of wilderness regions have been illustrated in Chapter 4. The following key questions also need to be considered:

- Should wilderness areas be protected?
- Are there additional areas which need to be managed? Where?
- To what extent have current management strategies been successful?
- What more needs to be done? Where, how and by whom should it be done?
- How will we know if this 'more' has been successful? What will be the success criteria?

- What models should be adopted for the future management of wilderness regions?

In this section you will need to address these questions and try to come to your own conclusions about the future for wilderness areas. Case studies will focus upon Scotland and Antarctica.

Wilderness in Scotland – the last remaining wilderness in the UK?

Unlike England and Wales, there are at present no National Parks in Scotland. This may be somewhat surprising in view of the landscapes, which are generally considered to be spectacular (Figure 5.1). Instead, the Scottish Natural Heritage and the Scottish National Trust play an important management role in control over upland wilderness lands in Scotland together with private landowners and voluntary organizations.

There have been proposals to establish National Parks in National Park Direction Areas since 1945. As there had been no National Parks Commission in Scotland, there was no official body to monitor and oversee development, and only a limited number of

▶ **Figure 5.1** Scottish wilderness.

private organizations had any concern for this spectacular countryside. Nothing happened until 1967, when the Countryside Commission for Scotland (CCS) was established to encourage conservation and recreation in over 98 per cent of the country. Its report in 1974 proposed four types of park:

- Urban Parks: the town park with an active role in recreation
- Country Parks: establishing 36 parks covering 6426 hectares
- Regional Parks: four parks were eventually established covering 86 125 hectares
- Special Parks: similar to National Parks in England and Wales, these would include the Cairngorms, Glen Nevis and Glencoe, Loch Lomond, and the Trossachs.

No headway was made, and opposition from landowners and local authorities prevented any progress. In 1978, partly in response to the lack of commitment, the CCS published 'Scotland's Scenic Heritage', in which 40 areas of high scenic value were identified. To these, they attached the term 'National Scenic Areas' (NSAs), which were recommended for preservation for their high scenic value. The proposals were accepted and the 40 areas shown on Figure 5.2 cover over 1 million hectares, or 13 per cent of the country. Figures 5.3 and 5.4 show the kinds of areas which have been identified.

▼ **Figure 5.2** 'Valued' areas in Scotland.

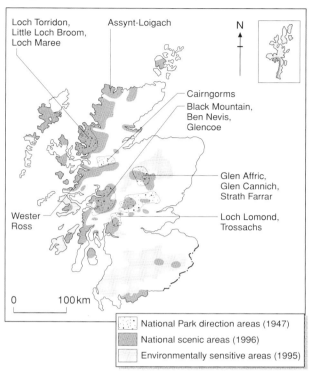

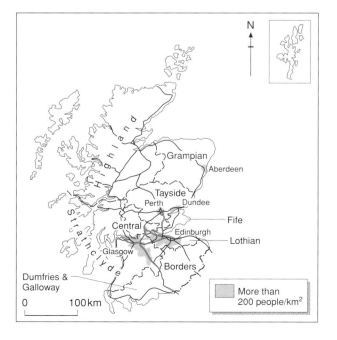

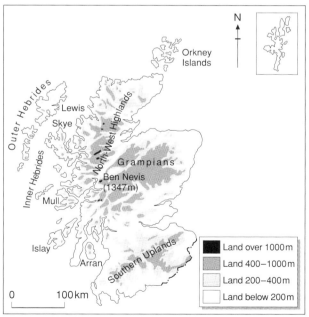

▲ **Figure 5.3** Relief regions in Scotland.

◄ **Figure 5.4** Political map of Scotland.

Within these areas, certain planning proposals had to be vetted by the CCS. Management agreements could be formulated by the CCS or local authority, often with discretionary payments to the local landowners. The designation, however, has been little more than a label. With the designation of the NSAs the former National Park Direction Areas ceased to exist. The NSAs, however, have had few positive benefits and have not generated funding, nor stopped inappropriate planning. Neither nature conservation nor recreation have a part to play in the role of NSAs.

There was renewed interest in the National Parks in Scotland in the 1990s with a report by the CCS, 'The Mountain Areas of Scotland'. The report proposed six areas for 'Park' status: Assynt-Coigach, Wester Ross, Cuillin Hills, Ben Nevis and Glen Coe, Loch Lomond and the Cairngorms (Figure 5.2). Political will was again lacking and no legislation was put in place to protect these areas. In 1991 the Scottish Council for National Parks was reconstituted as an independent voluntary body, and the Natural Heritage (Scotland) Act legislated for the new areas. In 1998 the SNH still had to present its criteria for the selection and designation of these areas to the government for approval. However, there are proposals for the designation of National Park to be given to Loch Lomond and the Trossachs and also possibly to the Cairngorms.

Form groups of two or three. Study Figures 5.1 to 5.4.

1 Produce an annotated sketch map which identifies areas you consider to be wilderness. Estimate what percentage of Scotland could be classified as 'wilderness'.

2 Which regions seem to be under most severe threat unless protection is established? Explain your choice.

3 What issues are raised about the nature of wilderness management in Scotland at present?

4 Which of the following management strategies do you consider to be the most appropriate ways of protecting Scottish wilderness regions:

a) National Parks/protected areas, which offer free entry to everyone

b) restricted access (if you select this option, you should say who you would restrict, why and how)

c) establishing payment for entry for tourist users

d) zoning, so that some areas are recognized for protection, while in others various levels of development are permitted?

Explain your choice.

How should wilderness areas in Scotland be managed?

It seems that there is little will among public – or government – organizations to become involved in the designation of National Park areas now. You might like to consider whether the new Scottish parliament will change this. There are alternatives, however. This study looks at the role of a voluntary organization – the John Muir Trust.

The John Muir Trust

The John Muir Trust was formed in 1983 to safeguard and conserve wild places and to increase awareness and understanding of the value of such places. The Trust is named after John Muir, who was born in Scotland in 1838 and emigrated to the USA as a child. There he established the World Conservation Movement and devoted his life to safeguarding the world's wild places for future generations.

At present the Trust owns and manages five areas in the Highlands and Islands of Scotland totalling 18 000 hectares (Figure 5.5). Its main aim is to bring Britain's finest wild landscapes into stable long-term conservation ownership. It is committed to the principle of 'thinking globally and acting locally'. It has 5500 members whose support is vital to the work of the Trust. The Trust works closely with local communities and it believes that sustainable conservation can only be achieved by recognizing and understanding the special qualities of wild places and the many aspects which make up wild landscapes. In 1996, it produced a policy, extracts of which are included in Figure 5.6.

▲ **Figure 5.5** Scottish wilderness owned by the John Muir Trust.

▼ **Figure 5.6** Extracts from the John Muir Trust's policies, July 1996.

1 Acquisition: The John Muir Trust's distinctive role is to safeguard whole landscapes of wild land. Specific selection criteria include:

- quality as wild land: remoteness, ruggedness, freedom from intrusions
- scenic quality: beauty, diversity
- wildlife and scientific interest: variety and rarity of species, and of geological features and landforms
- threats: such as inappropriate or unsustainable development
- opportunities: for ecological restoration, for good management, or for co-operation with other interests, including local communities.

2 Ownership: The Trust's main aim is to bring Britain's finest wild landscapes into stable long-term conservation ownership. Most of the landscapes are currently split into several ownerships, some of which change hands frequently. This brings a risk of environmental damage or changes of management which might be harmful. The Trust will put priority on (a) purchases of key holdings which will safeguard its finest features, and (b) purchases of additional land, or opportunities for co-operative management, that bring nearer the goal of unified management.

3 Partnership: Both in partnership and subsequent management, the Trust will seek to co-operate with others with interests in managing the landscape, e.g. communities, landowners (public or private), and conservation organizations.

4 Working landscapes: The Trust recognizes that these areas contain people living and working in wild places. It focuses on partnerships that will both sustain wild landscapes, and improve economic, cultural and social circumstances of local communities. It will share management with local communities, and have as its prime aim to retain, and where possible restore natural processes and indigenous populations of plants and animals. The Trust will therefore promote sustainable management, and repair physical damage that has resulted in declines in biodiversity, and deterioration of soils and landscape. The core recreational values of wild land relate to tranquillity, solitude and freedom. Access to visitors is not promoted, but informal access is open to all who wish to visit for quiet recreation or study.

5 Science: The Trust is committed to radical action to conserve and restore Britain's wild places. It believes that such action must be preceded by careful research and assessment; the Trust, therefore, needs to take account of the best possible ecological and social science.

6 Cooperation: The Trust views it as essential to work as far as possible with other interests, including owners, conservation bodies and local communities.

The areas under guardianship of the Trust are:

- Knoydart – where the Trust owns and manages over 1200 hectares including the mountain Ladhar Bheinn
- Skye – where the Trust owns the neighbouring Torrin and Strathaid estates, totalling over 8000 hectares, which extend into Loch Coruisk in the heart of the Black Cuillin and include the mountains Bla Bheinn and Marsco
- Sandwood – 4600 hectares, with highly valued beach and coastal scenery in Sutherland.

Other land is in the hands of private landowners, the National Trust, the Forestry Commission, the Ministry of Defence and the RSPB. One drawback for the long-term management of the landscape is that ownership by different organizations causes fragmentation of the land and only short-term solutions to conservation.

▼ **Figure 5.7** From *Geographical*, February 1995.

Return to the wild

The reintroduction of extinct native species has become enshrined in European law, specifically in Article 22 of the Habitats Directive which states that member states shall 'study the desirability of reintroducing species in Annex IV that are native to their territory, where this might contribute to their conservation.'

This coincides with the current shift in ideas of nature conservation: to move away from human management of small and incomplete ecosystems, and instead to create extensive wilderness areas in which its ecology is maintained by large animals and natural disturbances. 'I don't think you can run nature reserves in the future using masses of wardens and volunteers with chainsaws,' says Roy Dennis, the biologist, who led the restoration of the red kite and the sea eagle to Scotland. 'You need the animals that really crunch up the forest. We tend to think of a nature reserve as a beautiful place where none of the plants are touched and none

of the trees are damaged. But what we need is more death and destruction in the forest – not just renewal.'

Robert Moss of the Institute of Terrestrial Ecology believes that there are no biological reasons why the wolf, for example, could not be introduced immediately. 'Wolves are highly adaptable and could certainly survive in the Scottish Highlands,' he says, 'so long as people do not persecute them.' Farmers could be compensated for sheep kills, he argues, while the presence of wolves might trigger a return to more traditional shepherding with sheep dogs keeping watch over their flocks.

Whether achieved by wolf or by gun, one thing is certain: once grazing pressure is reduced, Caledonian forest has a real ability to regenerate. Where deer have been fenced out of enclosures in Glen Affric in the central Highlands, for example, hundreds of thousands of pine seedlings are appearing.

On the 125-square kilometre Abernethy Reserve in the northern Cairngorms similar things are happening. After it bought the land in 1988, the Royal Society for the Protection of Birds (RSPB) pursued a remorseless deer cull that has now halved deer numbers. As a result, millions of young pines, willows, birches and rowan trees are returning, both in existing forest areas and on open moorland. In this way, says reserve manager John Stewart, the RSPB is creating the 'New Wood of Caledon', a place where large mammals might be returned in the future.

The RSPB now owns some 400 square kilometres of Scotland, including its most recently purchased Forsinard estate in the Flow Country peatlands of east Sutherland. And it is

just one of a growing band of conservation landowners. For example, the National Trust for Scotland has recently purchased the West Affric estate, adjacent to the Forestry Commission's Glen Affric, and is negotiating to buy the Mar Lodge estate in the Cairngorms.

Will Woodlands, the mystery buyer of the Glenfeshie estate in the Cairngorms, also claims conservation objectives. And the John Muir Trust has just bought the 60 square kilometre Strathaird estate on the southern Isle of Skye, adjacent to its own Torrin Estate, bringing its total landholdings to 140 square kilometres.

Particularly where conservation estates join up to make yet larger areas, exciting new conservation opportunities loom. Abernethy, for example, is set to become a core forest area in a wider Cairngorms conservation area of some 2,000 square kilometres. It will incorporate the forests of Glenmore, Rothiemurcus, Glenfeshie and Mar, under a plan coordinated by Scottish Natural Heritage that recently won the approval of Scottish Secretary Ian Lang. This would be a unit more than big enough to bring back a wide range of extinct wild animals. The Forestry Commission's Glen Affric, likewise, could become the focus of a new forest area of some 600 square kilometres in the central Highlands stretching between the east and west coasts of Scotland.

In the Scottish Highlands at any rate, it is only a matter of years before habitat is in place for the release of extinct mammals. But are these broad-scale approaches to nature conservation to be restricted to Britain's wildest areas of undeveloped land? Or could they have a role in its densely populated, fragmented landscapes south of the border?

Future management of wilderness in Scotland

Read Figure 5.7 and the information about the John Muir Trust.

1 What part does scientific research play in environmental management?

2 Do you think that the UK Government should intervene in managing wilderness areas in Scotland? If yes, what action should it take? If no, what alternatives would you suggest for conservation of these areas? Debate this as a class with a motion for or against the designation of National Parks in Scotland, then write your final view in about 500 words.

What does the future hold for wilderness management?

The case of Scotland shows how long-term management problems can arise where protection is attempted by a variety of different organizations, since no long-term plan can be developed or implemented. The same problem arises elsewhere in the UK and also the USA, where the number of different organizations is even greater. Tracts of land within the USA, as we have seen in Alaska (see page 55), are designated as National Parks, refuges, forest parks and private land. The problem is that these areas are isolated from each other. Figure 5.8 shows how the problem of conservation 'islands' has left many species more likely to decline and become extinct, something which was never intended.

▼ **Figure 5.8** From *Time,* November 1997.

Archipelago EARTH

We think we can preserve nature on little islands scattered in an ocean of human dominion. It won't work. It's not enough.

By David Quammen

Forget about Marshall McLuhan's global village. Although it may have been a prescient idea as applied to electronic communication, from an ecological perspective it's diametrically wrong. McLuhan foresaw unity of culture and consciousness, but the defining trend among earth's ecosystems is the opposite: fragmentation. So far as nature is concerned, we live in a global archipelago. To say it more plainly, a world of islands.

As we humans have spread across earth's surface, we have transformed the great landscapes in two ways – by shrinking them overall and by dividing the remnants into pieces. Those pieces constitute ecological islands in an ocean of human dominion. The dominion takes many forms – crop fields and highways, forest clear-cuts and urban sprawl. The fragmentation grows worse each passing year. The islands are green, beleaguered and dwarfed by the immensity that surrounds them.

Some of them are familiar: Yellowstone, Yosemite, Royal Chitwan, Serengeti. Others are patches of forest, savanna or wetland. Many of their animal and plant populations are marooned. A grizzly bear in Yellowstone Park can't wander to Canada in search of a mate – not without running through the ranches and suburbs of late-20th century Montana. A tiger in Royal Chitwan, near Nepal's southern border, likewise can't make its way to a tiger refuge in India.

This phenomenon I call the island syndrome. It's the gloomy half of a good-news-bad-news deal that has made islands especially interesting to biologists over the past 162 years. The good news is that islands are conducive to the evolution of new and revealingly peculiar species – as Charles Darwin himself discovered. The bad news is that islands are deathtraps for many of the same creatures to which they give birth.

Because of limited area, an island holds a relatively small population of any animal or plant, and a small population is more easily wiped out. Within the past four centuries, by one tally, 171 species and subspecies of bird have gone extinct. Some 90% of those lived on islands. Island-bound mammals, reptiles and amphibians have also shown vulnerability. But now that the continental landscapes are being carved into fragments, the island syndrome is coming to the mainlands.

Several studies by William Newmark and other ecologists have shown that some national parks in the U.S., Canada and East Africa have lost populations of mammals to the island syndrome. These have been local extinctions within a given patch of landscape, not extinctions of an entire species; still, they represent ominous warnings of a

continued from page 67

worldwide trend and must be counted as failures in exactly those places we thought we had protected. If the lynx can't survive within Mount Rainier National Park, in Washington state, where can it survive? If the greater kudu and the sable antelope have vanished from Mkomazi Game Reserve in Tanzania, then what losses are occurring on those remnants of landscape that haven't received such statutory protection?

The island syndrome challenges one of the most basic assumptions behind humanity's halfhearted efforts at nature conservation: that we can save the rain forest, the dry forest, the panda, the elephant, the multifarious richness of species and ecosystems, by setting aside a few tracts of expendable landscape and calling them parks, nature reserves, refuges.

Truth is, we can't. It won't work. It's not enough. Nature is too interconnected. A species goes extinct, taking another species with it, and the consequences of their absence are felt by still others. When sliced into small pieces, ecosystems lose species and then – like tapestries – they tend to unravel.

Meanwhile, McLuhan's global village is also becoming reality, as advances in communication and travel carry Web sites, rap music, Marlboro ads., American TV and English-speaking tourists to every corner of the planet, pushing local cultures and languages to extinction. That McLuhanesque connectivity, with its homogenizing effect, turns out to be just as destructive, in its own way, as the island syndrome.

The dismal irony of our age is that these two seemingly opposite trends, cultural unification and ecological fragmentation, yield a common result: loss of diversity. The global archipelago will be a world that's starker, uglier, duller and lonelier for us humans as a species, and we'll all experience that loneliness together.

▶ **Figure 5.9** Extract from 'Return to the wild', *Geographical*, February 1995.

Since the last war, a process of agricultural intensification, road building and urbanisation has fragmented our valuable wildlife habitats – whether ancient woodlands, heaths, salt marshes, flood meadows or chalk grasslands – into isolated islands in degraded landscapes. Many of these islands are now protected. Some 60,000 hectares of Britain are managed by local wildlife trusts as nature reserves, preserving some 2,000 irreplaceable jewels of the countryside. And 3,800 Sites of Special Scientific Interest (SSSI) now cover 6.6 per cent of England – an area of nearly 9,000 square kilometres. These conservation efforts have been amazingly successful: out of the 88,000 species of life in Britain, only one mammal (the greater mouse-eared bat), one fish, two spiders, nine flowering plants and 35 insects have actually become extinct over the last 50 years.

But is this island approach to nature conservation sustainable in the long term? Not, according to Sarah Hawkswell, conservation officer with the Wildlife Trusts Partnership, who points out that isolated communities of plants or animals tend to die out over time. We have to look outside protected areas and the SSSI system, she says. 'The units are simply not big enough and if they remain as islands in the desert they will disappear.'

Leo Batten, a biodiversity specialist with English Nature (EN) agrees. 'Even the best managed sites may continue to lose species if isolated from other similar habitat patches,' he says. 'They are vulnerable to changes in land use and vulnerable to chance events. Habitat fragmentation may result in reduced populations, species extinctions and the immigration of species favoured by newly-created edges.'

Without action, says Hawkswell, a new wave of extinctions could be on the way. 'The numbers of many wildlife species have already dropped below minimum thresholds for long-term survival,' she says. 'Things may look safe enough from year to year, but the chances of small, isolated populations surviving for a century or more are very poor. We've got to get our act together now.'

Will the island approach to environmental management work?

Read Figures 5.8 and 5.9 and then answer the following questions:

1 What do you understand by the 'archipelago approach'?

2 Explain why this approach presents difficulties for environmental management.

3 With reference to a wilderness region you have studied, suggest to what extent you think that this approach has led to difficulties in conservation of that environment. How could the management be improved?

Is the 'island' approach (Figure 5.8) to nature conservation sustainable in the long term? Fragmentation may well lead to reduced populations, immigration and possibly extinction of species. These areas may require further protection measures. Figure 5.10 describes how English Nature has identified Prime Biodiversity Areas (PBAs) which aim to protect wildlife and habitats, and rebuild ecosystems where species diversity has been upset. This could mean reintroducing species which have declined in number. In Scotland, for example, wolves may be reintroduced (Figure 5.7) to combat overgrazing by deer, which causes young forest shoots to be consumed, preventing regeneration.

In response to the problem, EN (English Nature) has launched a new initiative to target so-called Prime Biodiversity Areas (PBAs) — areas of countryside with a particularly high density of good wildlife habitats. These PBAs, says Dr Batten, 'encompass clusters of protected habitats extending over wide areas of countryside where we can rebuild ecosystems and reverse fragmentation.'

Some 150 PBAs have already been defined in England, ranging in size from 10 to hundreds of square kilometres. Resources are to be targeted in PBAs, says Dr Batten, for two reasons. Firstly, they will deliver better conservation. By an ecologist's rule of thumb a single continuous area of habitat can contain double the number of species than if it is broken up into 10 separate pieces. In a large unit, any chance local extinctions can be replaced from other parts of the ecosystem. Secondly, says Batten, 'large PBAs should be more cost-effective to maintain per hectare compared to small isolated areas surrounded by a hostile environment. We have to look at where we get the most value for the resources we put in.'

Wildlife trusts are following a similar strategy, identifying the areas in which biodiversity is concentrated so that they know where to focus their efforts. This allows them to influence local development plans through the provision of countrywide 'alert maps' to guide the Countryside Commission's allocation of Countryside Stewardship Scheme funds and to help EN identify further PBAs.

We already have a model for this type of controlled wilderness in the New Forest. Made up of ancient forest, conifer plantations and heaths, medieval forest law and practice continues even today. This remains an example unique in Britain of a synergy between man, timber production, free-roaming livestock and ancient heath and forest, that has proved its ability to survive and maintain its biodiversity for over nine centuries.

Expanding these types of controlled wilderness areas would allow not only conservation but also evolution, effectively absent in our island nature reserves. And that is something that biodiversity conservation for the long term must surely encompass.

▲ **Figure 5.10** Extract from 'Return to the wild', *Geographical*, February 1995.

If current approaches to management are not sustainable, then we must consider strategies which are. Although countries can protect and conserve areas within their boundaries, it is becoming clear that national barriers around environmentally valuable lands or rich biological reserves are not the solution. The next section shows how attempts are being made to manage the problem internationally.

The Earth Summit and Agenda 21

In 1992 the United Nations Conference on Environment and Development (UNCED) was held in Rio de Janeiro – now better known as the 'Earth Summit'. At Rio, governments adopted Agenda 21 as a 'blueprint for sustainable development'. A range of environmental, economic and social issues for global sustainable development were recommended, to be implemented nationally.

By 1994 over 100 countries had established councils, commissions or other bodies to develop a national Agenda 21, or sustainable development strategies. In the UK, this operates at local council level, where each council has to develop strategies to meet the requirements of Agenda 21. Despite little concrete evidence that there have been significant changes in policy nationally, a positive outcome of Agenda 21 has been an increase in local government and public awareness.

The Convention on Biodiversity at the Earth Summit, in which governments promised to protect plant and animal species, was signed by 158 countries. The Convention came into force on 29 December 1993 and now has 168 signatory countries, though the USA had still not agreed to sign in 1998. The treaty recognizes the value of genetic and biological diversity. By signing, countries agree to:

- take an inventory of their biological reserves
- establish, where appropriate, systems to protect natural areas
- undertake environmental impact assessments for proposed activities that are likely to affect biodiversity
- take measures to ensure that economic gain from commercial use of genetic resources are shared with nations from which those resources have originated (for example, particular plant species which originate in ELDCs may be genetically developed for commercial output in Western industrialized countries; a system of international copyrights or patents would prevent such economic development without 'royalty' payments to ELDCs)
- establish a fund to assist developing nations to implement the provisions of the Convention.

Buffer zones

How far can conventional National Parks be a solution to land protection in ELDCs? They may contain vital resources urgently needed by impoverished economies or hungry people. A possibility may be the development of buffer zones. Days when people were forcibly removed from their land in the interests of conservation are largely gone, and a new model allows indigenous people to live and develop within a strictly-policed buffer zone or conservation area.

This has been the principle of the Korup project in the Cameroon rainforest, the most diverse forest area left in Africa. The key is to extract natural resources without destroying either them or the landscape. Ecotourism seeks to fulfil this aim, as has already been shown in Chapter 4. National Parks within the UK also seek to achieve this, and may be more effective in environmental management than National Parks in the USA, which attempt to maintain the landscape in pristine condition under great duress, such as pressure exerted by mining companies. Parks might do better to fulfil the needs of local populations rather than expel them. In 1992, Martin Holdgate, former director of IUCN, the world's largest alliance of conservation scientists, suggested that a sustainable twenty-first century would protect the whole landscape – not as something untouched and pristine, but as something rich, diverse and alive. True conservation might mean the end of protected areas.

Global-scale protection: what should we do with Antarctica?

Antarctica, often described as the last great wilderness, is virtually untouched by human activity. Remote and hostile, it covers about 14 million square kilometres, or 10 per cent of the Earth's land surface (Figure 5.11). A permanent ice cap covers about 98 per cent of its land surface to an average depth of 2 kilometres and a maximum depth of 4.5 kilometres. Average monthly rainfall is about the same as in the Sahara Desert – that is, about 10 millimetres per month or less. The main ice-free areas lie around the coast, but in several places the ice cap extends off-shore in vast ice shelves. About 90 per cent of the world's fresh water is stored up in its vast ice sheet; were it to melt, global sea levels could rise by an estimated 55 metres.

Life on Antarctica is limited by the harsh physical and climatic conditions (Figure 5.12) to a few sea birds and lichens, mosses and mites on the protruding mountains and peaks (nunataks). However, seas around the ice cap are among the most fertile in the world, supporting over 50 species of sea birds, marine animals including six seal species – comprising two-thirds of the world's seals – several whale species (including blue, fin, sei, humpback, sperm and right whales) and about 100 species of fish.

In summer, increases in marine algae support vast numbers of krill which form the base of the Antarctic food web. Krill is the main food source for five whale species, three species of seal, twenty species of fish, three species of squid and many species of birds including penguins.

Antarctica plays a vital role in moderating the world's weather and climate, and holds essential information for climatologists and scientists studying the Earth's evolution and atmosphere. Ice cores, representing millions of years of compacted ice, hold the history of the Earth's climate and show changes to the composition of the atmosphere. Trapped air bubbles record the changes in the proportion of carbon dioxide in the atmosphere, which is fundamental to an understanding of global warming. Ice cores have shown an increase in radioactivity and lead pollution in the atmosphere since 1945.

What are the threats to Antarctica?

Figure 5.13 shows the extent of international claims upon Antarctica, and Figure 5.14 may help to explain why the continent is such an object of attention. Huge mineral reserves are thought – and in some cases known – to exist. Countries with established claims to political territory have staked an interest in its future.

▼ **Figure 5.11** Antarctica.

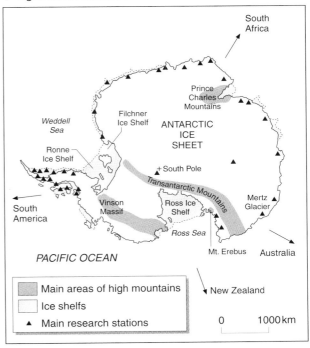

▲ **Figure 5.12** Wilderness landscape in Antarctica.

▶ **Figure 5.13** The distribution of claims upon Antarctica by seven countries.

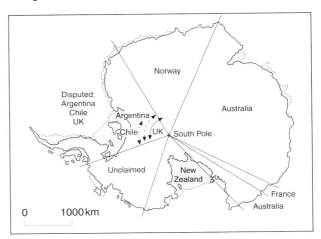

At a less dramatic level, consider Figures 5.15 and 5.16. Settlement on Antarctica is far from dense, but is significant. Figure 5.15 shows one of the bases on Antarctica and the waste it generates. Bases vary in purpose – they may be for defence or scientific research. While its permanent and temporary settlers are not anything like the mass seasonal influx of people to National Parks in the UK or USA, pressure is increasing to manage the issue before it develops further. The environmental effects of settlement may include destruction or modification of habitats, changes to the distribution of organisms, introduction of alien organisms, pollution by noxious substances, change to the heat balance and aesthetic change. Figure 5.16 shows issues which arise as a result of scientists working on Antarctica.

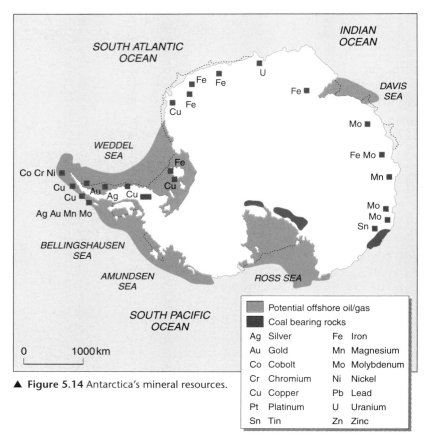

▲ **Figure 5.14** Antarctica's mineral resources.

▼ **Figure 5.15** Waste generated by a scientific research base on Antarctica.

▼ **Figure 5.16** Some of the management issues faced by Davis Base, a scientific research base on Antarctica.

Non-indigenous species
A permit is required to bring any animal, plant, virus, bacterium, yeast or fungus that is not indigenous to Antarctica, except if it is to be used as food. It is also an offence to let any organism brought in to escape into the environment.

Power
Fossil fuel consumption for power is a source of atmospheric pollution. At Davis Base electrical power is generated by four diesel motors coupled to generators in the main power house. There are also two emergency generators.

Field trips, huts, depots
During the summer months visitors increase, many carrying out research expeditions from huts and tented camps in the field. In the winter research continues but to a lesser extent. The excellent scenery of the Vestfold Hills, the coast and penguin colonies in addition to good sea-ice conditions make it a very popular base.

Sewage
All new buildings have a piped sewage treatment system. All human and water waste is treated and discharged into the ocean. There are several gas-fired toilets. Solid treated residue is deposited in tidal cracks in the sea-ice in winter.

Management Issues

Water supply
Water is mainly supplied by melting drift snow which is very energy consuming and alternative sources of fresh water are currently being sought. A secondary system involves pumping water from a small tarn in the station area. This water is below WHO standards as it is rich in minerals and is mainly used for washing. Daily consumption is around 120 litres per person.

Use of vehicles, roads, routes and vehicle access
Problems created by noise, exhaust, fuel spills and vehicle movement have potential for damage to scientific data collection, deterioration of vegetation, damage to ecological formations and disturbance of wildlife. Vehicles are restricted to established tracks. Davis Base has approximately 2 kilometres of roadway and three heavy vehicle bridges. Snow clearance in winter produces additional problems.

Aircraft operations
All birds and seals are disturbed by aircraft and care is taken at vunerable stages in the life cycle. Exhaust and fuel lost during refuelling can affect lakes and vegetation. Helicopters are also used in summer. An airstrip is not considered economically or environmentally viable at present.

Waste dumping
Increasing amounts are tipped on to sea-ice or tip site. Waste dumping into sea is no longer practised except for waste from sewage treatment. Tip was regularly burned off and remaining waste was not combustible, e.g. glass, steel. The policy now is to return as much waste as possible to Australia. A high temperature incinerator is also available.

Other activities are truly international in nature. The influx of huge Japanese fishing and whaling factory ships is just one pressure; technology has allowed other countries to seek and plunder the rich Antarctic fishing grounds (Figure 5.17). Meanwhile, what qualifies as science? Are all scientists on Antarctica researching Earth history, or are some seeking mineral reserves within its unusual geology?

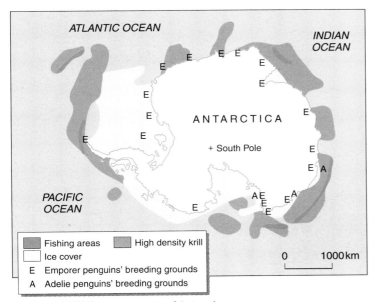

▲ **Figure 5.17** Ocean resources of Antarctica.

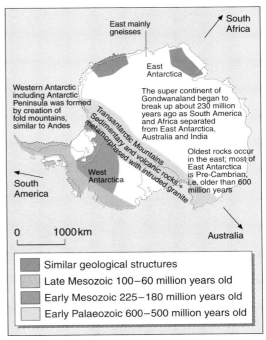

▲ **Figure 5.18** The geological significance of Antarctica.

Form groups of two or three, and study Figures 5.15–5.18.

1 a) Make a copy of the table below and complete it. Consider the different kinds of activities (two have been suggested) and the impact that each makes on Antarctica – political, social, economic, cultural and environmental.

b) Activities may have positive or negative effects. Use a highlighter pen on the final table to identify positive or negative effects in different colours.

Activity	Location	Description of impact	Extent of impact	Duration of impact
Mining				
Scientific research				

2 a) Copy the table below. List each impact which you have identified in question 1, and suggest measures or monitoring programmes that could be implemented in order to minimize the impact further.

   b) Discuss your suggestions with other groups. Do all groups agree?

Impact	Measure to minimize impact

3 Now make a copy of the evaluation matrix opposite. Complete it as follows:

   a) For each activity which you have identified as having a negative impact on Antarctica in question 1, select a different coloured pencil or pen and place a cross along the continuum line for each criterion on the matrix. Include a colour key for each activity.

   b) When you have completed each activity, join the dots to obtain an overview of where each activity is placed along the impact line.

c) Which activity seems to have the greatest impact? Why?

4 a) List activities which you think should be allowed to continue in Antarctica. Why do you think that these activities should be allowed?

   b) Which activities should not be permitted in Antarctica? Why?

   c) What changes would make them more acceptable? Explain.

   d) Are there other criteria which need to be part of the evaluation process?

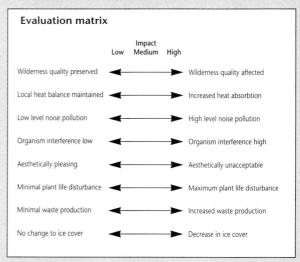

Evaluation matrix

Impact: Low — Medium — High

- Wilderness quality preserved ←→ Wilderness quality affected
- Local heat balance maintained ←→ Increased heat absorbtion
- Low level noise pollution ←→ High level noise pollution
- Organism interference low ←→ Organism interference high
- Aesthetically pleasing ←→ Aesthetically unacceptable
- Minimal plant life disturbance ←→ Maximum plant life disturbance
- Minimal waste production ←→ Increased waste production
- No change to ice cover ←→ Decrease in ice cover

How optimistic is the future for Antarctica?

In 1959 the Antarctica Treaty (Figure 5.19) was drawn up to establish a set of guidelines for the present and future management of Antarctica. It came into force on 23 June 1961 with twelve signatories. There are now 42 signatories. But does the Treaty go far enough?

Other attempts have also been made to introduce guidelines, such as CRAMRA, (Convention on the Regulation of Antarctic Mineral Resources Activity) established in 1988 to manage mineral resources. However, France and Australia did not sign and later proposed a conservation convention in the Madrid Protocol in 1991. The Protocol on Environmental Protection to the Antarctic Treaty designates Antarctica as 'a natural reserve, devoted to peace and science'. These ensure that activities undertaken are consistent with the protection of the Antarctic environment and ecosystems for the next 50 years. Oil and mineral exploitation are prohibited. The Protocol was signed in Madrid by the 26 Consultative Parties on 4 October 1991.

▼ **Figure 5.19** A summary of the Antarctica Treaty.

Article I: Antarctica shall be used for peaceful purposes only. The establishment of military bases, conducting military manoeuvres, and the testing of military weapons shall be prohibited. Military personnel and equipment can be used for scientific or other peaceful purpose.

Article II: Co-operation and freedom for scientific investigation shall continue.

Article III: Information from scientific research programmes, personnel and observations and research findings shall be exchanged between nations to allow maximum efficiency and economy of operations.

Article IV: No new claims, or enlargement of existing claims to territory in Antarctica shall be made.

Article V: Any nuclear explosions or disposal of radioactive waste are prohibited.

Article VI: Treaty includes area south of 60°South, including all ice shelves, but excludes seas which are subject to International Law.

Article VII: Contracting parties can designate people to become observers. These observers are known to other parties and have freedom of access at any time to all areas within Antarctica. Areas include all stations, installations, equipment, ships and aircraft at points of embarking and discharging cargoes and personnel.

Article VIII: Observers are under jurisdiction of their national party.

Article IX: Contracting parties shall meet at suitable intervals to exchange information, consult on matters of interest and make recommendations.

Article X: Each contracting party undertakes to exert appropriate efforts to ensure no-one engages in any activity which contravenes the principles and purpose of the present treaty.

Article XI: If a dispute arises between two or more contracted parties, they will endeavour to come to a peaceful solution through negotiation. If it cannot be resolved, the dispute will be referred to the International Court of Justice for settlement.

Article XII: The Treaty can be modified or amended at any time by unanimous agreement of the contracting parties. The Treaty shall be reviewed after 30 years.

Article XIII: The present Treaty shall be subject to ratification by the signatory states. It shall be open for accession by any State which is a member of the United Nations or any State invited to accede to the Treaty with the consent of all the contracting parties.

Article XIV: The present Treaty shall be deposited in the archives of the US Government which shall transmit copies to the Governments of the signatory and acceding States.

Is World Heritage protection for Antarctica the solution?

Many of the nations involved in Antarctica feel that the Treaty is sufficient protection as it is flexible enough to evolve. Some countries, such as New Zealand, have suggested that Antarctica should be designated a 'World Park', protecting the continent for ever. As there is little support from other signatories, Greenpeace have suggested that the World Heritage Convention be used. A World Heritage Site is protected, conserved and rehabilitated if damaged. Rights of ownership are not removed, nor is the right to decide on land use, as long as World Heritage values are upheld.

For an area to be designated as a World Heritage Site it must fulfil the following criteria:

- be an outstanding example representing major stages of the Earth's history
- be an outstanding example of significant ongoing geological processes, biological evolution or human interaction with the environment
- contain outstanding natural phenomena, formations or features, or areas of exceptional beauty or combinations of natural and cultural elements

- contain the natural habitat of threatened plant or animal species of important scientific or conservation value.

Some examples of places already designated as World Heritage Sites include:

- Galapagos National Park, Ecuador (1978)
- Grand Canyon National Park, USA (1979)
- Sagarmatha National Park, including Mount Everest, Nepal (1979)
- Great Barrier Reef, Australia (1981)
- Serengeti National Park, Tanzania (1981)
- Yosemite National Park, USA (1984).

In groups of three or four, read through all the information you can on Antarctica and decide whether or not you think that Antarctica would fulfil the criteria to be classified as a World Heritage Site. Justify your ideas.

A futures wheel

A futures wheel is a method used to decide between various options for the future of a location. It is a visual way of deciding the best outcome. It is useful to identify the positive and negative outcomes. In addition, look for economic, social and environmental options.

1 Using the example in Figure 5.20, draw a futures wheel for Antarctica. Identify the positive and negative features.

2 What do you think would be the best possible outcome for Antarctica?

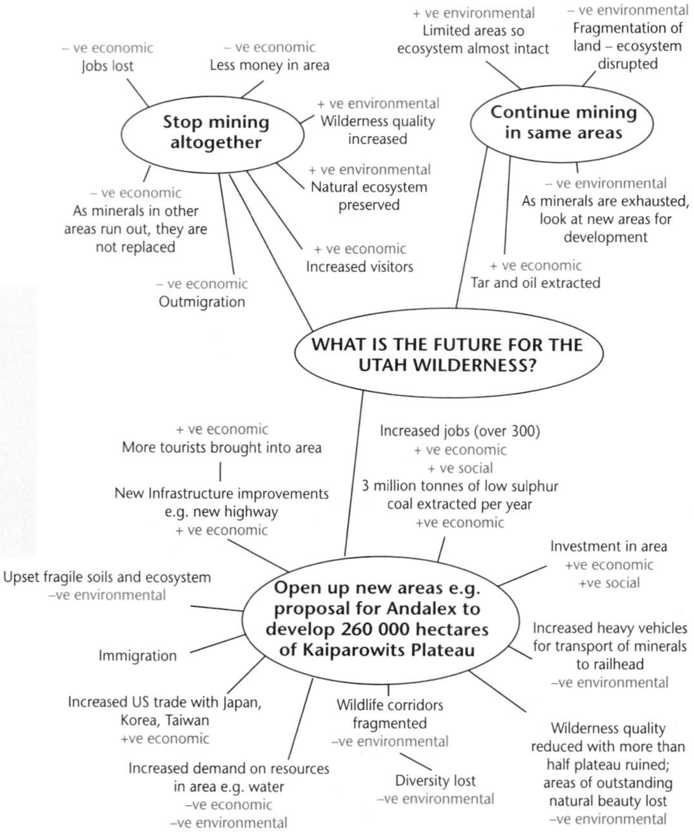

+ve Positive factors (economic, social or environmental)
–ve Negative factors (economic, social or environmental)

▶ **Figure 5.20** An example of a futures wheel for the Utah wilderness.

Stop mining altogether
– ve economic Jobs lost
– ve economic Less money in area
+ ve environmental Wilderness quality increased
+ ve environmental Natural ecosystem preserved
– ve economic As minerals in other areas run out, they are not replaced
– ve economic Outmigration
+ ve economic Increased visitors

Continue mining in same areas
+ ve environmental Limited areas so ecosystem almost intact
– ve environmental Fragmentation of land – ecosystem disrupted
– ve environmental As minerals are exhausted, look at new areas for development
+ ve economic Tar and oil extracted

WHAT IS THE FUTURE FOR THE UTAH WILDERNESS?

Open up new areas e.g. proposal for Andalex to develop 260 000 hectares of Kaiparowits Plateau
+ ve economic More tourists brought into area
New Infrastructure improvements e.g. new highway + ve economic
Upset fragile soils and ecosystem –ve environmental
Immigration
Increased US trade with Japan, Korea, Taiwan +ve economic
Increased demand on resources in area e.g. water –ve economic –ve environmental
Increased jobs (over 300) + ve economic + ve social
3 million tonnes of low sulphur coal extracted per year +ve economic
Investment in area +ve economic +ve social
Increased heavy vehicles for transport of minerals to railhead –ve environmental
Wildlife corridors fragmented –ve environmental
Diversity lost –ve environmental
Wilderness quality reduced with more than half plateau ruined; areas of outstanding natural beauty lost –ve environmental

The whole essay: planning

One of the ways to ensure an essay is successful is in the planning stage. It is necessary to introduce the essay, develop ideas and then conclude it. Each stage has been referred to in previous chapters. Now that you have a variety of case studies from local to global level, from places at different stages of the economic development process, you can address geographical ideas and generalizations in a complete essay.

The essay for this unit should be completed in about 45 minutes, so careful planning is essential. Practise under timed conditions. Allow five minutes for planning, showing your ideas in a brainstorm-type diagram, and then organize your thoughts by numbering points. Tick the points as you write, and allow time to read and check the essay at the end, and add any extra points.

As you become more dependent on word processing in your day-to-day work, the organization of thoughts becomes more crucial. In an exam, it is not easy to reorganize thoughts and paragraphs within the essay, without the end product becoming messy and difficult to read. Figures 5.21 and 5.22 provide two examples of plans for the essay entitled:

'Why might the survival of wilderness areas depend upon international co-operation and agreement? Illustrate your answer with reference to a range of case studies.'

▼ **Figure 5.21** Essay plan 1.

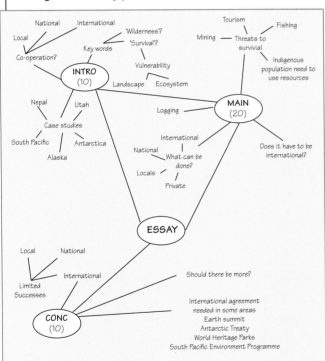

▼ **Figure 5.22** Essay plan 2.

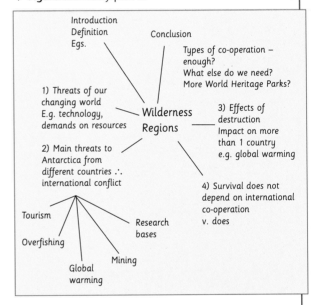

Study Figures 5.21 and 5.22 carefully.

1 Identify which of the two plans is more useful for writing this essay. Why?

2 What amendments would you make to either of the two plans?

3 Using your improved plan for this essay, write the essay under timed conditions.

Summary table for wilderness regions

On a copy of the table below summarize the key points of each of the case studies. It has been started for you.

Case study	What value does this wilderness have?	What management strategies are used?	Actual and potential conflicts	What conflicts are significant?	How successfully are they being managed?	What are the possible future management strategies?
Denali: local						
South Pacific: regional						
Antarctica: global						

Ideas for further study

1 Research the external threats to Antarctica such as (a) the impact of DDT on the food chain and (b) the effects of global warming. How can these threats be managed? (Look at the achievements of the Kyoto Summit of December 1997.)

2 Consider what information would be needed to evaluate the effectiveness of the management of a wilderness region.

References and further reading

J. Chaffey, *Managing Wilderness Regions*, Hodder & Stoughton, 1996.

J. Chaffey, *Managing Environments in Britain and Ireland*, Hodder & Stoughton, 1997 (Chapter 3).

R. Prosser, *Natural Systems and Human Responses*, Nelson, 1992 (Chapter 12).

R. Prosser, *Managing Environmental Systems*, Nelson, 1995 (Chapter 8).

Geofile, September 1991, January 1993.

Ecology and Environmental Science Fact Sheets, e.g. No. 4, September 1993, The Environmental Press, Birmingham.

Ecosystems and Human Activity, RSPB.

Publications by the British Antarctic Survey and Greenpeace.

Panos Briefing Publications, London, e.g. 'People and Parks', June 1997, and 'Ecotourism', January 1995.

Magazine articles are also extremely valuable. Look for articles in *Geography Review* (e.g. September 1992, May 1996, January 1997, March 1997), *Geographical* (e.g. March 1995, March 1997, April 1997, October 1997, December 1997), *New Scientist, National Geographic* and *Time*.

Managing Wilderness Regions: Summary

	Key questions	Ideas and concepts	Examples used in this book
Concept	• What are wilderness areas? • Where are they located?	1 Wilderness areas can be defined in terms of their remote location and physical characteristics, including harsh climate. 2 The concept of wilderness is relative and linked to a continuum. 3 Improved technology has made wilderness areas more accessible, e.g. transport networks, communication satellites, survival technology.	Papua, New Guinea North York Moors Nunavut
Processes	• What are the characteristics of wilderness landscapes and environments? • Why should these be conserved?	1 Wilderness landscapes contain landforms and ecosystems of outstanding global importance. 2 These ecosystems are especially fragile and vulnerable to exploitation and, possibly, irreparable damage.	Antarctica Papua, New Guinea South Pacific
	• How and why are people an important element of wilderness regions? • Who uses wilderness regions, and why?	1 Low population density is associated with harsh environments. 2 Such areas have traditionally only been occupied by indigenous peoples, but are increasingly sought after by resource developers – e.g. in forestry, mining, etc. 3 Conflicts may develop between indigenous people and resource developers.	Papua, New Guinea Antarctica South Pacific South Pacific
Pressures	• What are the pressures on wilderness regions? • How and why are pressures on these areas increasing? • How can such pressures be managed?	1 Difficult environments possess enormous potential in terms of their resources. 2 Improved technology and accessibility make resource development of wilderness areas increasingly possible and likely. 3 Sensitive or sustainable use is essential in order to conserve environmental quality. 4 The pressure of tourism affects wilderness areas increasingly; ecotourism may help to maintain wilderness quality.	South Pacific South Pacific Great Staircase Region, Utah, USA Denali National Park, Alaska, USA Arctic Wildlife Refuge, Alaska, USA Sagarmatha and Annapurna National Parks, Nepal
The future	• Should wilderness regions be protected and conserved? • What are the ways in which conservation can be attempted? • How and why might protection constrain or conflict with economic development?	1 The conflict between economic development and conservation may not be reconcilable. 2 Strategic thinking may be necessary to protect wilderness regions, and would require international agreement. 3 Wilderness regions may collectively or individually require management strategies for the future.	Scottish wilderness protection through Trusts National Parks protection through Trusts Wildlife refuges e.g. Arctic Ecotourism (see Chapter 4) Buffer zones – Annapurna Sanctuary, Nepal Global protection – Earth Summit, Antarctica

Index

Page numbers in *italics* refer to illustrations.